CARE *for the* CAREGIVER

Surviving
the Emotional
Roller Coaster

Dr. Sherry L. Blake

Care for the Caregiver
Surviving the Emotional Roller Coaster

Copyright © 2020 by Dr. Sherry L. Blake

ISBN: 978-1-7359310-0-5 (paperback)
         978-1-7359310-1-2 (eBook)

Published by:
Dr. Sherry Enterprises
Atlanta, GA 30349

Dedication

This book is dedicated to and is in memory of my parents, Mr. and Mrs. James and Carolyn Lester, for their unending love and support of me. Their love, support, encouragement and wisdom are my basic fiber and give me the strength to be who I am.

This book is also dedicated to the millions of caregivers who selflessly provide needed services to loved ones and others. Often these countless hours of care are given without any regard to the emotional, physical or financial cost to their personal lives.

Contents

Acknowledgments

I would like to thank God for continuing to provide me a platform to share my knowledge and experiences with millions of people. I would also like to thank and acknowledge all of my family and friends who have patiently waited for years as they listened to me talk about writing and needing to finish this book. Their patience and support have been unwavering.

A special thanks goes to my clients who have been caregivers and shared their struggles and triumphs with me. You taught me so much before I even dared imagine that, one day, I would have to embark on my own caregiver journey.

I could not possibly name everyone who has supported and contributed in some way to this project. However, a special thanks is extended to the following:

Victor J. Blake, MD — My dear husband and number one supporter. Your endless love and support are appreciated more than words can express. You are always the optimistic voice who reminds me that giving up is not an option and that we will always find a way no matter what.

Johnny "SirHiClass" Lester-Massey — My brand manager who created the Dr. Sherry brand that started as a small regional platform and now has grown into a national and international platform. He is the "all things Dr. Sherry" and pushes me to heights I never dreamed possible.

Linda Crutcher — My big sister who has always been there through thick and thin with her love and encouragement as well as her "Crutcher-isms." She has definitely kept me on track with this project by asking daily: "When will the book be ready?" or "Where is the book?"

Kennetra Price — My niece who unknowingly assures me that my mother will always live on through her parenting, humor, wisdom and love for family.

Dr. Marilyn Denise King — My "sister friend" who has taught me what friendship, sisterhood and unconditional love arc really about. Our friendship has stood the test of time for over forty years, laughing and crying together.

Karla Winfrey — My brilliant "go to" person for advice and to ask any question simple or complex. She has been telling me for years that I need to write this book and other things. I know I am in trouble when she starts the conversation with "I have been telling you...." I am forever grateful for her constant encouragement and support that keep me on track and moving in the right direction.

Pamela Carn — My patient and calm editor who listened intensely to my story and helped weave and shape it into this incredible book that will help countless caregivers and others. Her expertise and insight made this process easy and manageable, while she made sure my voice was clearly heard throughout the process. I am forever grateful for Ms. Carn teaching me to write in pictures and bringing visual life to my words.

Jerilyn Manning, Esq., Dr. Marcia Stokes, Denise Brown-Henderson, Esq., David Lester-Massey, Carlton Winfrey — My excellent preview reading team. Their attention to detail was essential. They have all been there with their expertise to challenge and support me throughout this project and all of my endeavors. I can never thank them enough for their truth-telling; and their tough love keeps me grounded.

Foreword

I am honored to write this foreword for *Care for the Caregiver—Surviving the Emotional Roller Coaster*, an important and inspiring work. I have known Dr. Sherry Blake my entire adult life. We became friends in the late 1970s, as we toiled through obtaining our undergraduate degrees in psychology at Tennessee State University. At the graduate level, she stayed the course in psychology, and I opted for a career in social work, yet, we both maintained a focus on mental health. Over the years, we have supported each other through many of life's ups and downs. And I witnessed her journey on the unpredictable ride known as caregiving firsthand.

As a gerontological social worker for the last 15 years, I have encountered many older adults and their loved ones, who care for them through an array of stages of later adulthood. Initially, my work with older adults involved conducting assessments of persons with Alzheimer's disease, dementing illnesses and memory loss in later life. Along the way, I incorporated "caregiver coaching" to address the unexpected process that caregivers experience while caring for their loved ones. That process involves a shift in understanding the chaotic emotions, as well as discovering the appropriate actions and transactions needed to become effective in carrying out the many duties of a caregiver. *Care for the Caregiver* successfully speaks to both the process and the multiple facets of caring for our aging loved ones. As a Caregiver Coach, I have accompanied many on the roller coaster of associated emotions and the enormous need for information and guidance for effective caregiving described by Dr. Blake.

Care for the Caregiver is a poignant retelling of a challenging transformation and winding path to resiliency. Dr. Blake made the painful, but necessary, transition from being a professional caregiver to clients, to being a personal caregiver to her parents. Indeed, her transition took her from offering advice based on the objectivity of research to offering irrefutable evidence based on personal experience. This is a riveting story that draws you in for the erratic ride of caring for aging parents—complicated by everything else that is going on in your life at the same time. Her commitment to her parents and dedication to providing the most effective care for them is both humbling and inspiring. The writing of this book is quite timely. Although based on her personal experience, the "graying of America" and facts regarding current life expectancy rates indicate that others will also make this journey and can benefit from the knowledge of her experience.

Dr. Blake provides tips for coping, questions to ask, identifies resources that are available to help meet your needs and offers suggestions to help you better manage your role as a caregiver. The consequences of providing care to aging loved ones have been well documented by research. Over time, as Dr. Blake can attest to, these stressful circumstances can become overwhelming and debilitating. This book helps you to prepare for the changes to come. The reality, challenge and responsibility of distance caregiving is also addressed. Above all, the importance of self-care and the acknowledgment of resiliency bring home the message that no matter how difficult, you can survive the caregiving roller coaster!

M. Denise King, Ph.D.
Associate Professor, Social Work, Lindenwood University and Gerontological Care Manager, Pathways for Aging

Prologue

S EVEN O'CLOCK IN the morning, and the sun was just coming up as I cruised down Tennessee's I-24 listening to the soothing, soulful sounds of Kim Waters on my car radio. The sole sounds of smooth jazz and tires rolling along the asphalt made me feel as though I was the only car on the road … sort of an "I am the captain of my ship" feeling. In other words, I was having a peaceful ride. And, yet, every now and then, a nagging spate of doubt, in the form of questions, rudely broke into my thoughts.

"Am I doing the right thing?" was the first invader.

"Yes, I know I am doing the right thing. Besides, what else could I do?" I answered myself with a shaky sense of certainty.

"Do I really have a choice?" made me grip the steering wheel a little tighter as I confronted the question.

"Choice? The obvious choice was a no-brainer," I asserted. "Someone had to make the final decision, and I am that person—like it or not."

I ended the nonverbal session with a sharp affirmative nod of my head, physically reinforcing my "made up" mind. Now, back to the sounds of smooth jazz.

Unfortunately, this internal question and answer session interrupted my peaceful jazz repeatedly like a broken record for miles. As the scenery outside my window transformed from skyscrapers to stately homes to barns, I mentally rehearsed my version of the family passion play that was set to go live at the end of my journey. All of my parents' future affairs were carefully documented on paper, and every sibling knew his or her role. It was going to be a long and busy day, but I had convinced myself that everything was going to be *OK*.

And then, my cell phone rang. It was my sister, Linda, hysterically yelling, "Where are you?"

I nervously responded that I was about an hour away and calmly asked, "Why?"

She screamed, "Hurry! Hurry! The police are at Mama and Daddy's house!"

"Oh, my God! Police?" I thought. In an effort of futility, I tried to get my brain to grasp the concept as my heart hammered against my chest.

"What's going on?" I asked, but Linda abruptly hung up the phone.

At that moment, with my heart racing and my thoughts racing even faster, I literally pressed the pedal to the metal and cut my arrival time in half. I whipped into my parents' driveway on almost two wheels!

As I leapt from my car and ran into the house, I was immediately struck by the calmness in the air and my parents' tranquil demeanor. My mother was sitting quietly in her favorite well-worn, gold La-Z-Boy recliner with her legs crossed at her ankles wearing her old, green, plush robe that zipped up the front. A large black Afro-comb was stuck in the left side of her half-combed hair as she fidgeted with her hands. My father was sitting calmly at the kitchen bar eating breakfast fully dressed in his black Sunday suit jacket, wrinkled casual khaki brown pants and black dress shoes. He seemed more engaged in spreading grape jelly on his half-burned toast than my arrival. My parents barely spoke and showed little expression as I greeted them and gave them a big hug. Puzzled, I rattled off a series of questions.

"What's happened?" "Why were the police called?" "Who called the police?"

Linda shot me a "my last nerve" look and said in a fed up voice, "Ask them."

My mother, in her best matter of fact voice stated, "I did. I called them."

"Why?" I asked, matching my tone to hers.

"Yes," she started, "I called them because I wanted the police to arrest all of our children because you all are trying to put us out of our own house."

She went on to inform me that she had told the police that they had a child in Alaska that the police needed to arrest, too. My father remained silent as he sat on his barstool, but nodded his head every now and then as an endorsement of everything my mother said. He continued eating his bacon and eggs and never looked up as he physically co-signed my mother's objections to their children's hard and stressful decisions.

I looked at Linda in disbelief. I didn't know if I should laugh or cry.

"This is incredulous!" I thought.

I took a minute to regroup before responding. With all the composure that I could muster, I reminded my parents why and where they were moving. I also reminded them how we had all agreed and talked about it several times. And I reminded them about their previous visit to their new home and the people we met there. After about an hour of back and forth with concerns and assurances, my mother settled down and, once again, accepted that she and my father were moving.

In my wildest dreams, I never imagined that parenting my parents through their latter years would be part of my story. The thought of my relationship with them transforming from daughter to caregiver never entered my mind!

(CAREGIVER'S TIP

This book contains content that may trigger strong emotions for those providing care to loved ones. Please take mental health moments and allow yourself time to walk away and regroup, if needed.

Introduction

Trust Me ... This Ride is Nothing

I CAN ONLY COMPARE the process of caregiving for loved ones to a gigantic emotional roller coaster ride with multiple high peaks, long, steep, bottomless drops and twists and turns that you cannot see coming or avoid. I remember my first really scary roller coaster ride in an amusement park in Nashville, TN. I was a teen and hanging out with a group of friends at Opryland Amusement Park. Looking from a distance, *Wabash Cannonball*, the newest tallest roller coaster, didn't look that tall or frightening. So, I eagerly joined in with the teasing and laughing at the friends who admitted that they were too afraid to ride. The ones who were scared decided they would watch the rest of us ride. We were so excited and couldn't wait to ride the *Wabash Cannonball*. We bragged about how we were going to hold our hands in the air and not even hold on. I became one of the ring leaders in talking smack and teasing the ones who were not riding. The closer we got to the roller coaster, the taller it looked, and the quieter I became. My fearlessness and bravado deflated like a flat tire.

One of my friends looked at me and said, "Trust me, this ride is nothing. It is *not* scary."

I wanted to believe her, but I began to have serious doubts as we drew closer to the *Wabash Cannonball*. However, I couldn't dare back down after laughing at the others who were too afraid to ride. So, I nervously buckled myself into the seat. The attendant came by to make sure we were all securely locked in. At that moment, my heart began to race, and I knew my friend had lied. This was going to be a really scary ride!

As the coaster lurched forward on the track, it quickly picked up incredible speed before the long, slow jostling ride up the first tall hill. The ride climbed higher and higher until I realized that I was above the trees. Just before I could comprehend my plight, the big drop happened, and I was turned upside down and slammed into the side of my seat. So much for not holding on! I screamed to the top of my voice and gripped the handlebar so tight that I could not feel my hands. I thought my heart would literally jump out of my chest. I kept my eyes shut for most of the ride–fighting hard not to wet myself or throw up everything in my stomach. I thought the ride would never end as I held on for dear life, but it did. I exited the coaster with both my emotions and my hair in disarray. And that pretty much describes how I felt during my emotional roller coaster ride as a caregiver—all messed up and holding on for dear life.

I Survived Being a Caregiver

Just like the roller coaster, the role of a caregiver does not appear scary from a distance. However, the closer you get to taking on the role of becoming a caregiver, the taller and scarier it becomes. The roller coaster ride of caregiving has a lot of high points, and even more low points. The difference between an actual roller coaster ride and the emotional roller coaster ride of caregiving is that you don't get off in two or three minutes laughing and talking about the thrill of the ride. In fact, you have no idea how long the ride will last. It may last days, weeks, months and, in many cases, years. My roller coaster ride of caregiving lasted well over 10 years. However, I survived and lived to tell the story.

CAREGIVER'S TIP

Caregiving is stressful. Women especially are at risk for the harmful health effects of caregiver stress. These health problems may include depression or anxiety.

(www.womenshealth.gov/a-z-topics/caregiver-stress)

While there were many days filled with laughter and smiles, there were always the perpetual rumblings in the background reminding me that things could change at any moment. There were also days in which I felt unbuckled and at risk of flying out of my seat midair. Indeed, there were times when I feared being totally derailed and questioned my sanity.

Then, there were days when I felt quite in control. That is, until I reached the tipping point of a long climb. Just as I would breathe a sigh of relief, the bottom would drop out, and I would plunge, free-fall, turning sideways and upside down.

Though, as frightening as my ride was, I learned important life lessons. Inner strength, gratitude, thankfulness, patience and serenity were among the top lessons learned. At the end of it all, I was humbled and honored to have been able to love and care for both of my parents, just like they had loved and cared for me. While you may not be able to get out of your caregiver coaster, you can definitely make it less frightening and stressful and a great deal more manageable if you understand what to expect and what is needed before the ride becomes unbearable.

My guess is that some of you may be thinking: "She doesn't know what I'm going through." Rest assured, caregiving is definitely something I can talk about both personally and professionally. As a clinical psychologist with more than 30 years of experience, I have spent years working with and supporting individuals and families caring for their aging loved ones. I have cried silently for and with them, as I passed them the box of tissues in my office. Yet, when I personally went through the process of being a caregiver, it became truly *real*, and I quickly realized how emotionally unprepared I was to step into that role.

To make matters more overwhelming, both of my parents were in need of care at the same time. I was an emotional wreck during my years as a caregiver, though my friends and family had no idea. I experienced every emotion imaginable while trying to present a calm and focused façade. Fear, anxiety, depression, frustration, exhaustion, confusion, anger and guilt rode shotgun in my coaster. I kept company with them all and, sometimes, all in the course of a day. And while there were days in which the emotional pain was debilitating and paralyzing, there were days sprinkled with smiles, joy, laughter and the type of calm you experience right before a storm. Regardless of how I was feeling inside, I managed to maintain the "Happy, I am fine." picture for my parents, my siblings, my husband and children, my friends and any others who were depending on me to be the strong one.

Caregiving allowed me to gain an immense appreciation for the incredible depth and intensity of the emotional pain of watching loved ones slowly fade away physically and mentally, while doing all you can to maintain their presence. I know that it sounds like a cliché, but I wish that I had known then, what I know now. Basic information of what to expect emotionally and how to prepare for my parents' decline would have been really beneficial. I realize that much of what has been written about caregiving has not been written about the emotional health of the caregiver and what tools and supports are needed to survive the process. What I have found is that much of the emotional distress is related to a lack of understanding of the nuts and bolts of identifying needs; organizing tasks; and managing through stressful decisions and situations.

My personal experience, as well as my professional knowledge, has inspired me to write this book about my journey as a caregiver. This book takes a close look at the emotional roller coaster ride and provides a guide for preparing for and surviving it. My goal is to provide you with useful and needed information that will reduce your emotional stress and prepare you for your journey. If nothing else, you will be able to laugh and cry as you learn and realize that you are not alone.

Not only did I survive the emotional roller coaster ride, I grew from it. It was an intense journey that lasted more than a decade–filled with a good measure of stress, anxiety and tears and moments of laughter. It was my unending love for my parents and their limitless love for me that kept me buckled in tightly. And it is that same love that gives me the strength to share our experience.

CAREGIVER'S TIP

The role of a caregiver is drastically underestimated. The sacrifices are numerous. In an effort to care for your loved ones, you can forget or fail to take care of yourself. The emotional toll is often ignored. The uncertainty, alone, can cause wild mood swings and bouts of anxiety.

Taking steps to relieve caregiver stress helps prevent health problems. Also, taking care of yourself helps you take better care of your loved one and enjoy the rewards of caregiving.

(www.womenshealth.gov/a-z-topics/caregiver-stress)

What is Caregiving?

Caregivers are people who help others with activities of daily living and/or medically-related tasks. There are two types of caregivers: paid and unpaid. The type of caregiver needed depends, in part, on the level of care the individual needs. The level of care generally falls into two categories: skilled and unskilled. Skilled care requires at least a minimum level of medical training. The amount of training required varies from state to state. Skilled care may range from a certified nursing assistant (CNA) to a medical doctor. Skilled care may also occur in the home or in a facility depending on the need and the preference of the patient or family, as well as their ability to pay. Skilled caregivers are paid. A caregiver who is not trained to provide medical care provides unskilled care. Family and friends typically provide unskilled care involving activities of daily living and are usually not paid.

Activities of daily living (ADL) are basic day-to-day self-care activities that are necessary for an individual to live independently. Self-care activities include, but are not limited to, personal hygiene, dressing, eating, toileting and mobility. These are activities we are expected to be able to do adequately each day.

Beyond basic ADLs, being able to perform Instrumental Activities of Daily Living (IADLs) is also needed to live independently. These activities include, but are not limited to, managing and taking medication, housekeeping, cooking or preparing meals and managing money. ADLs and IADLs help determine the level of care and support needed.

The longer people live, the more care they will require. In the first half of the twentieth century, people were not expected to live many years past the age of 65, even past the age of 55 during the early part of the century. With much better medical treatment and with people becoming more health-conscious, it is not unusual for people to live an active life well into their 80s, and sometimes 90s. However, when the health of loved ones declines gradually or unexpectedly, usually the first choice is to keep them in the home as long as possible. Typically, this means that a family member has to become the caregiver.

Becoming an unpaid caregiver is not a chosen career, but one acquired by default. I do not know of anyone who grew up thinking, "I want to be an unpaid caregiver when I grow up." Can you imagine working hard to achieve your goal of going to college and receiving a degree or certification, starting a family, or being at the peak of your career only to suddenly give up everything for the chance to ride the emotional roller coaster of a caregiver? No, it does not happen like that. Ready or not, many of you are unknowingly walking slowly towards the gigantic roller coaster of caregiving. And when you arrive, you will have no choice but to climb into your coaster and buckle up.

Baby boomers, including myself, make up the largest group of individuals faced with riding the roller coaster. Many are dealing with life transitions, such as work/careers, parenting, grandparenting, marriage, divorce and/or health challenges. The untimely and unexpected role of caring for parents or other loved ones can create multiple challenges and conflicting agendas due to the already existing demands on their lives.

Often caregivers are already squeezed and stressed beyond their coping skills from the multiple roles they play in life. When I approached the roller coaster, I had a booming career with significant media exposure; public speaking engagements; a private practice where employees' livelihoods were in my hands; a husband with a thriving professional medical career; children in various school and community activities; and a home to help maintain. Like others, I climbed into the seat of the roller coaster without any regard to what or how much was going on in my personal life.

Most caregivers definitely love and want to do the best for their loved ones, but are often "sandwiched" between caring for their loved ones and managing their personal and professional lives. This conflict can generate a sense of internal anxiety and guilt that they are too embarrassed and ashamed to talk about to anyone.

The roller coaster ride can be brutal at times. Caregivers are frequently stressed to the limit emotionally and physically exhausted. Regardless of how they feel, most caregivers push forward and continue the ride with little time to consider what is happening to them. There is a price to pay when this occurs. Burnout is a basic price. Psychological and physical difficulties often become part of the more expensive prices paid by caregivers when they do not practice self-care. Depression, anxiety, high blood pressure, insomnia and other stress-related issues are common among many caregivers. Not only do I know this professionally, but I personally experienced it when I became the primary caregiver for my parents who had lived independently until their mid-eighties.

Unspoken fear became a part of my ride. I was afraid of continuing the ride, and even more afraid of it stopping. Eventually, I adapted to the uncertainty of the ride, but remained terrified of the alternative of losing my parents.

Although I felt like I was on one long continuous ride, I came to realize that there were different caregiving phases that influenced the speed and unexpected turns. After analyzing my own journey and the experiences of many other caregivers, I discovered that there were common patterns that could be divided into three distinct phases. The caregiver's role may be or feel chaotic, but these patterns are apparent even when caregivers are unaware of them. There are specific aspects related to each phase. The phases, their attributes and how to maneuver through them became crystal clear *after* I went through the process and rode the caregiving roller coaster for years. I refer to the three phases as the **3Rs of Caregiving:** *Recognition; Reality; and Release.*

The 3Rs of Caregiving

The 3Rs emerged after years of working with countless individuals who were caring for loved ones. Although I saw common patterns in my clients' experiences, their structure and composition became clear after I went through the caregiving process myself. The patterns are related to recognizing, adjusting to and understanding the physical and/or emotional changes of your loved ones; identifying and providing what is needed at any given time; and coping with and accepting the ongoing multiple changes without losing control emotionally, while preparing to let them go. These patterns make up the **3Rs of Caregiving**:

Phase 1: *Recognition – Pre-Caregiving*
Phase 2: *Reality – Caregiving*
Phase 3: *Release – Post-Caregiving*

The *Recognition Phase* occurs as part of *Pre-Caregiving*. You see the giant roller coaster, and you prepare to get on, buckle up and take off. Your emotions are playing ping pong because you really don't know what to expect. Your heart may be racing, while your legs feel like lead or jello. Just like in any amusement park, in caregiving there will be a lot of distractions, conversations and noisy activities around you. However, you must focus on identifying what is going on with your loved ones and what is necessary to deal with their issues. You must collect information regarding the problem and make plans to address it. This phase is the beginning of the ride, and you know in your heart of hearts that there is much more ahead–and it does not all look good. There will be a multitude of situations that you will and must adjust to during this phase of the ride. Ready or not, the roller coaster ride is starting.

The *Reality Phase* occurs after the roller coaster ride has been going for a while, and the actual *Caregiving* starts. In this phase, you put into play all of the planning and preparation you did in the Recognition Phase. Decision after decision must be made. You know what the issues are, and you fight hard to hold on to your carefully laid plans. Yet, even though you may have settled into the ride, uncertainty still plays a large role in your life.

During this phase, you are at risk of losing your sense of self because you are trying to hold *everything* together. At times, your emotions may be overwhelming, and you may feel guilty for your feelings of resentment and anger about your situation as a caregiver. You will need to pull on every support system and effective coping skill you have to stay buckled in for the full ride.

The **Release Phase** involves **Post-Caregiving** when the harsh jostling of the ride can actually intensify. Emotionally, you are conflicted as you try to accept the inevitable loss of your loved ones. You are exhausted, but you think you see the end ahead. Just when you think the ride is slowing down, it swiftly takes off with more hills and turns to come.

There is a lot of work to be done in this phase, which involves releasing previous responsibilities and picking up new ones. You cannot begin to imagine all of the roles that may be required of you. Even though the actual caregiving of your loved ones has stopped, you must remain on the ride because there are accounts and family matters to be settled before your seat buckle will release.

Each of the 3Rs of caregiving has its own set of special challenges that catapults caregivers through a range of feelings. Some feelings may be unique to a particular phase of the roller coaster ride, while others may be common fixtures throughout the entire process. Just know that you are not the first, nor will you be last, to go through this process. With guidance, you will be able to arrive at the end of the ride—whole and intact.

PHASE I

Recognition – Pre-Caregiving Phase
Preparation ... Preparation ... Preparation

Chapter 1

The Journey Begins

T HERE IT WAS! *Standing taller and shinier than I could have ever imagined. The lights from the roller coaster only served to magnify its humongous size. I had seen the roller coaster from a distance, but it did not appear terrifying until I got near it. I can't deny that I felt anxious whenever I caught a glimpse of any part of the monstrosity. If only I had taken the time to think through what I was getting into before agreeing to ride.*

The Recognition Phase is the hardest phase to detect and accept emotionally. Before I entered this phase, there had been many cues and telltale signs that I was approaching the caregiving ride faster than I thought. Yet, like many others, I initially ignored all of them. I reassured myself that I had the tools and knowledge to deal with any issues that I may encounter. After all, I was a clinical psychologist who had worked with clients for years, telling them how to handle similar situations. Surely, I had a toolbox full of resources and skills packed and ready for my own experience.

Shortly after the ride started, I learned quickly that there is a big difference between reading research about caregiving and having the necessary skills to be a caregiver. When you experience caregiving, it gives you an entirely different perspective than just talking about it from research and data sources. Much of what you know and the tools you may think you have are tested to, and, in some cases, beyond capacity.

I didn't want to see or believe that something was changing or wrong with my mother or father. With my parents' aging process, the beginning of the changes was initially slow and subtle. This allowed me to pretend that everything was fine and hang onto denial as long as possible. If the onset of problems had been sudden or acute, I probably would not have had a chance to settle into or stay in a state of denial while I was approaching the roller coaster.

Denial serves an important role in your life. It is deceptively comfortable and allows you to mistake it for a safe zone because you do not have to acknowledge or do anything about the problem or pending problem. You may even expend a great deal of time and energy to avoid believing that a problem exists. Sometimes, you may even become angry when someone brings it to your attention. While denial is a "safety zone" of sorts, it is also a dangerous zone because it robs you of the precious time you need to prepare for your loved ones' care and the journey ahead.

When dealing with my parents, I tried to spend as much time as possible in the denial zone before I had no choice but to recognize and accept that there was a real problem. It was heart-wrenching when I exited the denial zone. And while there may be a myriad of reasons for your stay in denial, just know, staying only makes it more difficult to embrace the Recognition Phase.

In my case, it was my parents' outstanding social and verbal skills, as well as their strong emotional bond with each other, that made problems difficult to detect. They became very good at covering missteps for each other. My parents were very sociable and well-respected community leaders. While my mother was quite outspoken and opinionated, my father was somewhat quiet and reserved.

My mother loved high fashion. She loved dressing up and the attention and countless compliments she received. She often wore designer suits with big "church hats" to match. The more "bling bling" in the suit and the larger the hat, the more she loved it. My mother had a collection of hats that was larger than most women's collection of shoes. Hats, hats, hats—everywhere—in every shape and color you could imagine. She had blue hats, yellow hats, red hats, white hats, purple hats. You name the color, and my mother had it on her head. Some hats had long feathers; others sported short feathers; some had small bows, while others were adorned with gigantic ones. There were even hats with veils that covered her entire face. Yes, my mother was well-known in the family and community for her "church hats." The only problem was that my mother's hats were so tall and wide that they blocked everyone's view around her. She literally had her own "big hat" zone.

My mother's vibrant personality and strong verbal skills often overshadowed my father. Most people's first impression of my father was that he was very shy and did not talk much. They would later discover that he enjoyed talking and had a funny, dry sense of humor. My father did not seem to mind my mother being in the spotlight. He often joked and said, "You know your mother is always going to have something to say."

My parents loved people, especially family and friends. Given we lived in a small town, everyone was family or friends. The aroma of great home-cooked food always greeted you as you approached my parents' door. They welcomed everyone, and the house was frequently full of family, friends, lots of food and laughter. They never met a stranger and seemed to know everyone. Growing up, I honestly thought they secretly worked for the FBI. They could rattle off the family history and any significant information about any guy in whom I had expressed an interest. They both had incredible memories and would frequently laugh and tell stories about past community or family happenings. They were not computers, but, I suspect, between the two of them, my parents mentally held as much data as any typical hard drive.

My mother and father had a very active social calendar filled with church and community activities and/or activities with family and friends. They were parents to anyone who needed love or a shoulder to cry on. Very little changed for them when my siblings and I became adults and moved out of the house. Grandchildren or other children for whom they were cooking or caring replaced our constant presence. And we all had house keys and returned home frequently to visit.

A sign ...

Years of great family gatherings with lots of fun, laughter and delicious food had passed before there was any indication that something might be changing cognitively with my mother. It was first brought to my attention when my father wrote me a letter stating, "Something is wrong with your mother." This moment was significant not only in his message to me about my mother, but in the fact that this was the first and only letter my father had ever written to me. He explained that she did not remember attending the funeral of a very popular pastor and friend in the community. In fact, he indicated that she argued with him that no one told her that the pastor had died. This was not only alarming for my father, but it was alarming for me. I called my mother to investigate what my father had written to me. My mother glossed right over the issue and minimized my father's concerns. She laughed and reminded me that my dad could "half hear" and that he hadn't heard her clearly. She convinced me with her cunning verbal skills that my father had somehow gotten what she said twisted around. When I spoke back to my father, he didn't agree with my mother, but he let it go. In the meantime, my siblings, who lived near our parents, were unaware of any of our father's concerns.

My father's letter was truly the first indication that I was standing in the roller coaster line. Considerable time passed before I would hear about other things that would suggest that my mother's memory was declining. Usually, things that she had forgotten would be told in a humorous manner. Given that we all forget things from time to time, I laughed along with everyone else. Looking back, these "little things" were actually alarm bells ringing out that something was wrong. Oh, but I was camped out in denial along with my siblings. I spoke with either my parents or siblings almost daily, and things seemed "just fine," for the most part.

Another sign ...

My parents took great pride in keeping my children as well as their other grandchildren during the summer school break. Their house was truly an informal summer camp with plenty of home-cooked meals and day activities and trips to different venues with cousins and friends. The children did everything from horseback riding to gardening to going to amusement parks to attending Vacation Bible School at church. There was also plenty of running and playing outside in the fresh open air of the beautiful country landscape. Regardless of how much fun they had, my parents ran a tight camp, and there were chores to do. Each of the children had daily responsibilities that were non-negotiable. Putting up your clothes and keeping up with your socks and other personal belongings were a few of them. Being ready on time to leave for church was also a non-negotiable. I knew that I did not have to worry about my children when they were with my parents. They had plenty of cousins and friends to play with and plenty of wholesome activities to keep them occupied.

Summer after summer, my children had a great time. I spoke with them on a regular basis, and they would give me the latest update of what was going on. While I missed them, I knew they were having fun, and I truly enjoyed the break from everyday parenting. Summer at their grandparents' house was a ritual that continued for years until the aging process began to take a toll on my parents.

As I stated before, denial is dangerous, and it definitely allowed me to rationalize things that made no sense and prolonged my dealing with the inevitable. It had been at least three years since my father's "Something's wrong with your mother" letter, when I came to pick up my children from a summer visit and attend a family reunion. I was flabbergasted when I saw my son's appearance. As he ran to give me a hug, his body odor and big smile of yellow teeth greeted me ahead of his hug. He looked like an abandoned child who was lost on the streets. He smelled and looked as if he had not had a bath or shower or brushed his teeth in weeks. His clothing was dirty and disheveled, and his hair was uncombed and desperately needed cutting. Instantly, I knew something was seriously wrong. Most of his clothing at the house was scattered or lost. I actually had to go shopping and buy him everything from underwear to sneakers before we could attend the family reunion the next day. I also helped him scrub down from his head to his toes.

Truthfully, I was more confused than upset. I knew something was not right. Nothing made any sense to me. My parents had always been strict about hygiene and keeping things in order. I began to wonder if my son had actually been with my parents for the summer or had he spent time somewhere else. However, I knew this couldn't be the case because I spoke with him and my parents almost daily.

When I asked my mother and father what happened, they seemed oblivious to the cause of my concern. My siblings couldn't provide any explanation either and only made matters worse by accusing me of overreacting. They even told me that my son was old enough to keep up with his own things and bathe himself daily. I had to pause and calm down as I questioned if I was indeed overreacting. Yes, my son was nine years old at the time, and maybe, I was overprotective and doing too much for him. So, once again, I let the obvious go and continued in my "uncomfortable" comfortable state of denial.

After that incident, I made a conscious effort to visit my parents as frequently as possible. For the most part, everything seemed the same during my visits. From time to time, the house would not be as neat and clean as usual, but my mother always had an explanation. She would laugh and tell me how one of the grand or great-grandchildren had pulled things out or spilled something. After talking to my siblings, we decided to help clean the house on a regular basis, given that both of our parents were aging. My father didn't mind, but he teased us about our mother complaining about our helping out.

My mother often reminded us that she could clean and take care of her own house. She constantly complained that my sister was throwing away all of her things. True enough, my sister would get rid of unnecessary things quite quickly. Because everything would be spotless when my sister finished cleaning, missing items were not noticed until days later. Our regular cleaning sprees became less frequent after our mother's constant complaints.

And another sign ...

My state of denial was totally shattered several months later when my mother started repeating herself. She would tell a story, and about five minutes later, she would repeat the exact same story. The first time I noticed her repeating herself, I thought it was an isolated incident. Her repetition became more frequent over the months. Initially, I would tell her that she just told me that.

My mother would quickly laugh and say, "Good, you heard me. I was just checking to see if you were listening."

My mother used her strong social and verbal skills to deflect most things that she did not want to deal with. This talent, combined with her sense of humor, made it difficult to clearly identify when things were wrong.

As time passed, her memory was noticeably declining. She was forgetting things more frequently and repeating herself more often. She was not attending church every Sunday although she would argue that she had. When I questioned her not attending one Sunday morning, she laughed and said she had attended enough church in her life to "carry her into Heaven" and missing that one Sunday was not going to keep her out of Heaven. My mother loved attending church, so frequent absences were a telltale sign that something had changed.

In addition, the house was not as organized or clean as usual, and her personal hygiene was declining. I asked my father and siblings if they had noticed any changes including an increase in her repeating herself and memory loss. They all acknowledged that from time to time they had noticed things, but they did not seem alarmed. As time passed, there were other signs of diminished capacity, but a plausible explanation was given every time I made mention of her behavior. My sister agreed with my concerns sometimes. However, she still thought that I was overreacting because I did not live in the area, and I was not around on a daily basis.

My mother's memory was definitely deteriorating, but her gifted social skills were sharp and masked issues. My father was extremely protective of her and resisted the idea along with my siblings that there was a serious problem staring us in the face. While trying to address my mother's issues, I noticed that my father's health and mental status were also slowly deteriorating. However, his memory decline appeared to be taking an expected slow pattern consistent with the aging process. On the other hand, my mother's cognitive functioning was quickly declining and inconsistent. Regardless, there were major health problems with both of my parents that needed to be addressed.

Given that they had been married for more than 60 years, they were masters at covering for each other's shortcomings. Yet, they would individually tell me about problems with the other one. When I would question something about my father, my mother would give a big smile, make a funny facial expression, and circle her index finger beside her head, and say, "You know your daddy's mind is gone."

In the meantime, if I questioned my father about my mother, he would say, "You know your mama is not right. Sometimes she makes no sense."

Although my siblings and I would laugh at things that our parents would say or forget, it really was no laughing matter. We did not initially realize that the parents we knew and loved were both slowly slipping away.

My mother would become defensive when I pressed issues. In African American families, you don't get to press your elders much before you are quickly put in your place. This attitude prolonged a formal diagnosis from being made much earlier. However, I finally realized that I could no longer ignore my mother's memory loss and overall mental deterioration, and, consequently, I relinquished my hold on denial.

It dawned on me that, in order to get my mother to accept the help that she needed, I might have to use the Power of Attorney (POA) that my parents had given to me more than 10 years earlier. I also realized that my ride on the emotional roller coaster was not going to be easy and that I might truly be alone at times. I experienced incredible fear and anxiety as my stomach did back flips, and I screamed internally.

It really didn't matter that I felt as though I were jumping out of my skin from stress and anxiety, I knew that I had to prepare as quickly as I could, regardless of what siblings or well-intentioned others thought. Having Durable Power of Attorney (POA) gave me the legal rights to make health and business decisions on my parents' behalf. A POA is essential and legally necessary for the decision maker and primary caretaker. As POA for my parents, my role was to fight for what was in their best interest and carry out their wishes.

As I stated earlier, my parents gave me their POA many years before their health started to decline. I did not ask or campaign for my role. My parents requested it. I accepted their offer without truly understanding the seriousness of the role or the reality that I would ever need to exercise it. When it became necessary to invoke my role as POA, carrying out the responsibilities was made even more challenging in that I lived out of state and had four siblings. Without question, my siblings were involved in our parents' caregiving to varying degrees, but I made the final decisions.

So, why me? My parents knew without question that they chose the child with the "most mouth" to be their representative. I was the one who was always questioning, negotiating and pushing the limits. Growing up in an African American Southern Baptist family, being an outspoken child was problematic at home and in the community, given that it was commonly believed that children should be seen and not heard. I broke all the rules by being seen and heard. I verbally fought for things that I wanted and challenged everything that I thought was unfair. Thank God, I had two parents who were supportive and patient with me challenging and exploring new heights. At times, they just looked and listened to me in disbelief or with sheer confusion.

For example, the day that I told them that I was going to attend graduate school to become a doctor, their bright, proud smiles quickly changed to confusion when I told them that I was going to be a clinical psychologist.

Their response in unison was "What? A psychologist? I thought you said you were going to be a doctor."

After explaining that I *was* going to be a doctor and what a psychologist does, they hesitantly gave me their blessings and support, even though they had no earthly idea what I would really be doing. Neither of them had ever known or met a psychologist, especially an African American one. What they did know was that I was determined to cut a path to achieve my goal regardless of the challenges.

Without question, I believe that my parents gave me their POA because of my determination to hold people accountable, as well as my unwillingness to give up and accept things as status quo. They knew that I would fight relentlessly for them when the time came. Let me make it clear, it is not that my other siblings would not fight for them, but my parents knew that I would not back down from anyone. It was this set of characteristics that my parents felt was necessary for their primary decision maker and caregiver to possess. Once I let go of denial and acknowledged the truth of my parents' condition, I knew that it was going to take all the strength and fight my parents saw in me and more to ride to the end.

CAREGIVER'S TIP

Before you agree to accept the role of **Power of Attorney**, make sure that you are prepared emotionally to be the "bad guy" at times. You will be criticized and judged on many of your decisions. You must be willing to do what is in the best interest of your loved ones.

Be prepared to swim against the tide.

Chapter 2

Recognize Pending Problems

E VEN BEFORE THE *roller coaster started, I could feel my anxiety building because I knew something was about to happen. My parents' functioning abilities were obviously changing. Although it was clear as day, I seemed to be the only one expressing concerns. Despite all the changes in my parents, everyone else in my family seemed to be in total denial. I knew my parents' health issues were not going away regardless of how many excuses were made. I also knew that I had to help my siblings get beyond denial in order to deal with these looming health issues.*

When I initially told my siblings that I believed that our mother had Alzheimer's Disease, it was if my statement had gone in one ear and out the other. Although I clearly presented her history and symptoms as I would any other patient, they remained in total denial. While they acknowledged that she repeated herself and forgot things sometimes, they were convinced that it was just a part of aging and that she was fine. They brushed me off as if I were just their sister Sherry ... not their sister Dr. Sherry, the professionally trained, doctorate-licensed psychologist.

Several weeks later, when my husband, a medical doctor, told them the same thing, they did not brush him off. Although my parents' diagnoses were clear to my husband and me, I had them confirmed independently through a comprehensive medical examination by each of their physicians. The result–both of my parents were suffering from a form of dementia. My mother was officially diagnosed with Alzheimer's and my father with vascular dementia.

Screaming into the wind ...

Even though my siblings understood intellectually our parents' mental health status, they remained emotionally stuck. Somehow, they still expected our parents to be as sharp and independent as they had been some 30 years ago. Their resistance made managing the process harder for me. While my siblings may have been stuck emotionally, my emotions were all over the place. I felt as though I were riding the roller coaster all by myself. Often, I felt uncontrollable tears streaming down my face. Tears of sadness would dissipate and quickly become tears of anger and frustration, as I climbed another hill in trying to do what was right by our parents without the full support of my siblings.

Denial had ceased to be an option for me. As problems and issues continued to emerge, my sister released her hold on denial. This left us with three brothers tightly clinging to denial like a life line. The roller coaster was getting faster with higher hills and sharper curves. I was screaming into the wind that we have a major problem, but no one was listening.

My mother's cognitive functioning sharply declined and became even more inconsistent as days passed. I would usually call my mother two, if not three, times a day. I typically spoke with her in the early morning on my way to work. Sometimes when I called her midday, she would state that she had not talked to me all week and that I must have forgotten that I had a mother. I knew clearly that she did not remember our conversation of a few hours before.

My parents' willingness to allow anyone into their home became a safety issue and a real concern for me. My mother would welcome anyone who came to their door. She befriended some Jehovah's Witnesses who visited on a weekly basis. However, neither my siblings nor I realized that our parents really did not know them. One Saturday morning when I arrived at my parents' home, a trio of Witnesses was sitting, laughing and talking with my parents. As I spoke, one of the ladies said it was nice seeing me again. I smiled and thought that I vaguely remembered seeing her on a previous occasion. However, it wasn't until I started listening to their conversation that I realized the purpose of their visit. I somewhat abrasively interrupted and said that my parents were Baptists and active leaders in their church. The Witnesses seemed a little taken aback, and then, my mother broke through in a clear and determined voice to set the record straight. She clarified that she knew that she was a Baptist and had been a Baptist all her life and that they were welcomed in their home, but she had no intention of changing her faith or church. While I fought to keep from laughing out loud, the three ladies gathered their booklets and hurriedly left the premises.

As the months passed, it became obvious that my parents were slowing down and that the aging process was taking its toll. The spark of energy was fading from both of them. There were times when my mother was noticeably less active and more forgetful. It was heart-wrenching to watch my mother nod off to sleep in the middle of the conversation and the activity around her. The well-dressed feisty mother at the center of my life was gradually fading into the background. I did not know this person who did not have a quick response to everything and everybody. I could tell when she was having a better day by her level of awareness and her efforts to be involved in the conversation. Sadly, those days became fewer and fewer.

My father's dementia was also apparent. Given that my father was naturally quiet, his decline in functioning was less noticeable. He often seemed to be in his own world. He would forget things and was easily confused. My father was seen a few times by the neighbors in the driveway or in his car late at night for no apparent reason. On one occasion a neighbor encouraged him to go back into the house and cautioned him to be careful being outside so late at night.

Both of them had become easy targets for telephone scams and sales people taking advantage of older people. I discovered how my parents had been taken advantage of financially by scammers near and far. I would get one problem resolved only to discover another one. My father unknowingly bought merchandise and enrolled in expensive programs over the phone. At one point, my parents purchased new windows for the entire house at a cost of over $15,000. They had no idea that they had actually signed a contract.

The frequency of 911 calls from my parents' home increased due to the need for medical attention as a result of their impaired judgment. I repeatedly told my siblings that our parents' abilities to function independently were compromised and that some changes were needed for them to remain at home.

I found myself crying alone in frustration about these problems that kept cropping up. I was unable to sleep, irritable and eating everything in sight. I knew I was sad and scared about what was ahead, but I had to keep riding. And so, I ignored what I was feeling and put on the strong, happy face for my family, my friends and my clients.

CAREGIVER'S TIP

Instead of just putting on a brave face when you are feeling vulnerable and overwhelmed, take a deep breath, focus and become brave. Dig deep within to find the courage to face your fears and anxiety so you will be strong enough to do what is needed.

Being "in charge" ...

Having the POA, definitely made me the "Bad Guy" with
my siblings. Regardless of the fact that I had regular family
meetings to get their input and include them on all decisions,
they knew that I had the last word. After all, I was the one
who personally checked and questioned what was going on
daily. This new relationship with my siblings was somewhat
awkward when I first took control of some of the decisions for
our parents. When I made requests of my siblings on behalf
of our parents, I held them accountable. A sore point with my
siblings was that I was often giving directives to everyone,
but I was not physically there. I understood their feelings,
but I knew I could not allow their underlying resentment
deter me from doing what was in our parents' best interest. I
was physically there as much as possible. In fact, I put more
than 90,000 miles on my car in less than three years driving
between Atlanta and Nashville.

I was keenly aware that I was on the caregiving roller
coaster regardless of what I was doing or where I was. Much
like my mother, I had become a wearer of "big hats." Yet, my
hats were adorned with stress and worry, rather than feathers
and bows. I tried to maintain some sense of normalcy with
my husband and children, my clinical practice and my public
and media appearances. In fact, work was a small escape
from the reality of my roller coaster ride.

Yet, I knew at any given moment I would be jostled back
to reality with a telephone call from Nashville. My heart
lurched every time my cell phone rang and flashed a Nashville
number across the screen. I had to force myself to take a

deep breath before I answered. The calls would always be about something that my parents had done that required my attention or input.

Frequently, the ambulance service was called to the house. Once, it was because my father fell when he attempted to climb through the window to open a locked guest bedroom door. No one stayed in the bedroom, and there was absolutely no need for him to try and open it. In the end, he was not seriously hurt, but he did sustain some minor injuries.

Given that my parents were still living alone, it was hard to get a clear, consistent picture of what was going on and what was needed. I felt like I was putting a giant puzzle together without having all the pieces.

For example, I would get one piece of the puzzle regarding them not taking their medications. Then, I would find out days later that they were no longer prescribed a particular medication. It would be unclear as to which medications they were supposed to be taking; or if a doctor (and which doctor) stopped or changed a medication; or when actual changes in their medications had occurred. To make matters worse, my mother was quick to self-diagnose and decide that she no longer needed to take a particular medication.

Old medications would be mixed up with new ones. There was no clear schedule of when or how often a medication was to be taken. My parents kept all their bottles of medication together in one big bag. It was like a grab bag of discarded drugs from a pharmaceutical company. This was not only very challenging, it was extremely dangerous. When I questioned my parents about their medication, my mother refused to answer me and directed her response to my father.

"James, do we look crazy or something?" she snapped.
"Sherry acts like we don't know what medicine we have. We
know what medicine to take. The doctor did give it to us."

In order to figure out the puzzle and what was needed, I
decided to just stop and spend time observing and collecting
information. As scary as it was on the roller coaster ride,
I had to stop screaming into the wind and take charge of
what was going on around me.

(CAREGIVER'S TIP

When it comes to managing your loved ones'
medications, it is best to speak directly to their
doctor and obtain an accurate list of all medications, prescribed and over-the-counter. Write down
what they are for and when and how they should
be taken. Discard all other medications in your
loved ones' possession. Develop a medical journal
to record medications taken and other important
information, such as dosages, any allergic reactions,
change in behavior, etc.

A little C & C goes a long way ...

It was obvious that my parents needed help, but they clearly
didn't know or want it. My siblings would tell me that they
had tried to help, but they couldn't because our parents would

not allow them. They often asked me what they needed to do and how did I know for sure what our parents needed?

These are common questions within families that are in the Recognition Phase. Even before the official diagnoses were made, the big unspoken question in our family was "What is needed for their care?" Which can also be translated into: "Who is going to care for them?" It was the elephant in the room that everyone pretended not to see. I could not ignore it because the elephant was sitting beside me as I sped downhill on the roller coaster of caregiving.

It was during these times that I first realized that C & C were my best friends. If you are wondering who C & C are, they are *Coca-Cola* and *Chocolate*—any kind of milk chocolate, especially with nuts. C & C were with me everywhere—at work and on the road. They stayed up with me late at night and comforted me as I cried and stressed out. As my anxiety and fear increased, my *human* friends would bring C & C over to visit with me.

One of my friends makes the most delicious chocolate brownies with nuts in the world. These brownies literally melt in your mouth. When she brought me brownies, I only shared a few with my family and hid the rest for myself. I needed and wanted all of the C & C I could get.

While C & C helped me maintain my coolness on the outside (for the most part), I knew that I needed more to help me manage my internal stress. During this time, my theme song became **Love & Favor** by John P. Kee & New Life. I quickly renamed the song, *"You Don't Know My Story,"* which is the hook in the song that the incredible LeJuene Thompson sings. It seemed like every time I turned on the radio, the song would be playing. It became the number one song on my playlist. I sang and cried along to my theme song day in and day out. It even penetrated my thoughts when I was giving presentations or simply talking with others. A smile would cross my face, and I would think, *"You don't know my story."*

Chapter 3

How to Prepare—"Must Do" Things

R EGARDLESS OF HOW stressful I may have felt, decisions had to be made. First things first, I had to determine what was needed for care. Often people's idea of care only focuses on the physical needs, but preparing for care should also include financial and emotional needs, as well as Activities of Daily Living (ADLs) needs. To answer the question of what is needed for care and other issues in the Recognition Phase, five steps are required.

Five (5) Steps of Preparing for Care in the Recognition Phase:

1. Identifying and understanding the problem
2. Completing a needs assessment of ADLs & LADLs

3. Locating essential documents
4. Developing a care plan
5. Identifying a support system(s)

Step 1: Identifying and understanding the problem

The process of identifying and understanding the problem is critical because it is the foundation for the need for care. The earlier this is done, the better. When changes in your loved ones' cognitive and behavioral functioning are initially detected, close observation and collaboration with others are needed. Once the changes are confirmed by a trusted group of observers, a professional examination should follow. It is important that you or someone else who is familiar with your loved ones escort them to their doctor's appointment. Not only do you need to take them to the doctor, you need to accompany them into their doctor's office. Explain to your loved ones before you arrive that you want to go with them when the receptionist or nurse calls for them to see the doctor. While in the doctor's office:

- Make sure you take copious notes—so, remember to bring a pen and a notebook with you to the appointment.
- Bring all of the prescribed and over-the-counter medications that they have been taking with you.
- Be prepared to provide as much medical history as possible.

- Make sure all the changes you and others have observed are written down and reported to the doctor. It is important to have the changes written down, along with the dates the changes were first observed.
- Go over the medications you brought to see what is necessary at this time. Get clarity on the frequency and time each medication should be taken.
- Ask the doctor as many questions you need in order to have a clear understanding of the diagnosis and what is needed.
- Make sure your loved ones ask any questions they may have.
- Write down in your notes the current diagnosis; any changes in medication; any directions or recommendations; and the date and time of the next appointment.
- Make sure the date and the name of the doctor seen are written on the top of the page.
- Make sure that you (or your designee) sign your name at the bottom of the page of notes.
- Keep and carry this notebook to all medical appointments.
- Make sure the notebook is kept in a safe location at home. This notebook becomes your loved ones' *personal medical journal* and will be very helpful and valuable during the caregiving process.

Step 2: Completing a needs assessment of ADLs & LADLs

Activities of Daily Living (ADLs) are basic day-to-day self-care activities that are necessary for an individual to live independently. These include, but are not limited to, activities related to personal hygiene, dressing, eating, toileting and mobility. These are activities we are expected to be able to do adequately each day.

Beyond basic ADLs, being able to perform Instrumental Activities of Daily Living (IADLs) is also needed to live independently. These activities include, but are not limited to, managing and taking medication, housekeeping, cooking or preparing meals and managing money. ADLs and IADLs help determine the level of care and support needed. The needs assessments are simple, but must be answered honestly in terms of your loved ones' abilities to perform. Examples of needs assessments checklists on pages 54 and 55 are from **SeniorPlanningServices.com.**

Activities of Daily Living (ADL)

ADL Function	Independent	Needs Help	Dependent	Cannot Do
Bathing				
Dressing				
Grooming				
Oral care				
Toileting				
Transferring bed/ chair				
Walking				
Climbing stairs				
Eating				

Instrumental Activities of Daily Living (IADL)

IADL Function	Independent	Needs Help	Dependent	Cannot Do
Shopping				
Cooking				
Managing medications				
Using the phone and looking up numbers				
Doing housework				
Doing laundry				
Driving or using public transportation				
Managing finances				

In addition, financial questions and access to resources must be answered. Such as, do your loved ones have the funds to cover the cost of their home, household expenses and medical care?

(CAREGIVER'S TIP

Caregiving is needed when the individual can no longer perform Activities of Daily Living (ADL) and the Instrumental Activities of Daily Living (IADLs). The earlier you consider the "who, what and where" of caregiving for your loved ones, the easier it will be later.

Step 3: Locating essential documents ("The Easter Egg Hunt")

Once the need for care is established, it is necessary for you, as the Power of Attorney (POA), to get organized and gather essential documents from your loved ones. This information will be asked for on multiple forms as you attempt to acquire help and resources. The checklist below identifies some of the basic information that you will need to compile:

Document Checklist
- __ Durable Power of Attorney
- __ Date of Birth
- __ Social Security Number
- __ Birth Certificate
- __ Marriage Certificate
- __ Death Certificate (deceased spouse)
- __ Military Records
  - __ Document DD214 (Certificate of Release or Discharge)
  - __ Enrollment Date
  - __ Branch of Military
  - __ Discharge Date
  - __ Type of Discharge
  - __ Disability Information
- __ Driver's License/Organ Donor Card
- __ Will
- __ Living Will
- __ Medical History
- __ Health Insurance Cards
  - __ Medical

___ Dental

___ Vision

___ Healthcare Providers

___ Primary Care Physician's Name

    ___ Phone #

    ___ Location

    ___ Medications

    ___ Prescriptions

    ___ Pharmacy

        ___ Phone #

        ___ Location

___ Insurance Policies

    ___ Life

    ___ Disability

    ___ Long-term care

    ___ Homeowners/Renter's

    ___ Automobile

    ___ Burial

___ Financial Records

___ Bank Accounts

    ___ Savings

    ___ Checking

    ___ Investment

___ Safe Deposit Box

    ___ Bank Location

    ___ Keys

    ___ Authorized Names

___ Phone Numbers of Close Relatives

___ Funeral Home Information

The most critical document is the Durable Power of Attorney (POA). A Durable POA gives you the legal rights to make decisions about both health care and business decisions on behalf of your loved ones. You cannot make any decisions on behalf of your loved ones without having POA. If at all possible, have your loved ones sign the Power of Attorney before they become ill. An honest conversation about whom they want to give POA and their desires should take place as soon as possible. If your loved ones are not capable of assigning the POA, you may have to seek legal consultation. Medical doctors or officials in any area will not share *any* information nor allow you to make *any* decisions on behalf of your loved ones without a copy of the POA. The same holds true when managing your loved ones' finances. In my own case, it was necessary to have the POA on file at the bank and my name on my parents' checking accounts and other banking information to conduct their financial business. This may sound minor, but without a POA you cannot even get a copy of your loved ones' utility bills although you may be paying the bills.

In fact, I kept a hard copy of my POA with me most of the time and a copy on a thumb drive all of the time. Again, it is important to acquire all of the applicable items on the Document Checklist because you will be asked to provide information from these documents multiple times on different forms. As POA for your loved ones, it is essential and smart to maintain good business records with receipts for financial transactions. Keep all of these documents organized in a folder clearly marked "Confidential and Important Documents." The file containing these documents should be kept in a safe and secure area. Many people may not be aware of this, but a POA is *only* effective while your loved ones are alive. *POA dies when your loved ones die!* Therefore, it is necessary to be legally assigned the executor for their estate in order to complete remaining business matters on behalf of your loved ones. Executorship can and should be assigned while your loved ones are in good health or as soon as possible.

On the hunt ...

It would have been extremely helpful if my parents' important papers had been neatly organized in a central logical location. Of course, my experience was just the opposite. My parents, like many elderly African Americans, had a tendency to hide important things inside of other things or under or behind other things. They called this "putting things up." And they did an excellent job of it!

Looking for and finding my parents' important documents reminded me of a big Easter Egg Hunt with well-hidden eggs! In many cases, it was like finding the proverbial needle in a haystack. This task became even more challenging as their health continued to decline and their needs increased. Initially, I searched and gathered up what I considered basic documents because I didn't know what I needed. As soon as I thought I had gathered all the eggs, the hunt would start again with several more eggs out there—somewhere—for me to find. It took an inordinate amount of time to locate and/or secure duplications of needed documents. It became apparent that I *must* get organized and map out the most efficient and effective way to handle my parents' affairs. Otherwise, I soon would become too physically exhausted and emotionally drained to be of any use.

The intensity of the roller coaster ride gripped me tightly as I used my Power of Attorney to make tough decisions for my parents. I slept less and less and grinded my teeth in my sleep. Sadness often overwhelmed me as I put on the happy face for everyone else. I loved my parents dearly and knew I had no choice but to settle down and stay buckled up as the wheels of my coaster rattled down the track. They had put their trust in me and were depending on me to do what was in their best interest until the end.

I found myself crying many days as I read through their personal documents. Initially, I felt awkward–like a child finding out things her parents never wanted her to know. The invasion of privacy was both essential and uncomfortable. I found most of the items, but I had to go through a long administrative process with the court and other agencies in order to secure the rest. The more information you know and have up front, the easier it will be later on.

My ideal scenario was that once I had gathered all of the pertinent information, my siblings and I would sit down and develop a care plan together. That was my ideal, but not my reality, especially since my brothers were still in denial.

This meant that I had to push forward at times with limited input from my siblings. It was during these times when I felt most alone on the roller coaster.

Step 4: Developing a care plan

Once all the information is gathered and reviewed, a care plan must be developed. A care plan is basically a written outline of what is needed; who is responsible for what; and how the responsibilities will be carried out. It should be based on an honest assessment of your loved ones' ADLs and IADLs, as well as available resources and other vital information. A care plan is fluid and not static. It changes as the needs of your loved ones change. At the time my parents needed a care plan, they were still living independently at home and resisting support every step of the way. Nevertheless, I developed a care plan and put the necessary supports in place for their level of need. I discussed the care plan with my siblings and our parents so that everyone heard and understood the same information.

Knowing that my parents needed help with some of their ADLs and IADLs, I hired a couple, Mr. and Mrs. T., who they liked and knew from the community. I hired them part-time and clearly identified tasks that I needed them to do each day. They were to arrive early in the morning, cook breakfast, clean up, administer my parents' medications and prepare lunch before leaving. Although my parents had known Mr. and Mrs. T. for years and enjoyed their company, they passively resisted them coming into their home. If Mr. and Mrs. T. were scheduled to arrive at 7:00 a.m., my parents would get up much earlier, cook and eat their breakfast and report that they had taken all of their medications before the couple arrived.

My mother would laugh and tell them how nice it was to see them, but that their daughter was wasting her money

CARE FOR THE CAREGIVER

having them to come. (The latter part was in reference to me.) My mother would also feed this same line to my siblings and me. Some of my siblings agreed with her, yet went along with my decision.

A "hot" breakfast ...

My siblings' denial of the seriousness of our parents' needs remained intact until the day of the fire. The smell of bacon grease and biscuits greeted Mr. and Mrs. T. at the back door that morning. As usual, my mother had gotten up early and cooked breakfast before their arrival. My mother opened the door with a big welcoming smile as she told them to come on in and have a seat because they had already eaten. She also assured them that she and my father had almost finished cleaning the kitchen, and there was really nothing for them to do. Though, she was glad for them to come by to visit.

My mother and my dad were laughing and talking with them about the latest gossip in the community when Mrs. T. noticed that the smell of bacon grease was getting stronger. She casually walked over to the kitchen and glanced to make sure nothing was left on the stove. Everything appeared to be in order with the exception of a few dishes in the sink. As they continued to talk, Mr. and Mrs. T. noticed the smell of grease had gotten even stronger. This time when Mrs. T. went into the kitchen, she made sure the stove caps were completely off. They were off, but she noticed the oven was on high. When she opened the oven door, she was met with a plume of black smoke and a big blaze of fire. My mother

62

had placed a skillet of bacon grease in the oven and turned it on "High."

Mrs. T. barely escaped the fire. She rushed to call 911 as Mr. T. tried to get my parents out of the house. He first got my father out, but soon realized that my mother had disappeared. The fire was blazing as Mr. and Mrs. T. frantically ran through the house calling out my mother's name. They found her hiding in her bedroom closet. As they were getting her out, my father tried to reenter the house to look for my mother.

The fire department arrived and extinguished the fire. The kitchen was heavily damaged, but everyone was safe. When my sister called me about the fire, my mother demanded to speak to me. She told me how Mrs. T. had made such a fuss about the fire. In her words, "Mrs. T. had made a mountain out of a molehill." My mother further surmised that it was obvious that Mrs. T. didn't cook or know how to cook because it was nothing more than a little grease fire.

I had to laugh to keep from crying. When I arrived at my parents' house, the smell of smoke met me before I could enter the door. The white stove was black from soot and pulled from the wall. It was dismantled with the cord thrown across the top. I was speechless, but very grateful that my parents were alive and that Mr. and Mrs. T. had been there on that fiery morning.

A change of plans ...

The fire was my breaking point. It made me stop everything, reevaluate and rewrite my parents' care plan. Obviously, having had Mr. and Mrs. T. assist them with their care at home for the past several months was not the answer. I had tried to be patient, but the fire was a rude awakening of how serious their situation was and how quickly they could have died. This realization made me clearly decide that they could no longer live independently. I had a meeting with all of my siblings to discuss our parents' condition and why their care plan had to be changed. They needed a different level of care. We needed to place them in an assisted living facility because they were no longer safe living alone.

The reality was that my siblings and I all worked full-time and none of us was in a position to quit work and move in with our parents full time. Neither were we in the financial position to hire a full-time staff to live in their home 24/7. Given this reality, the best option was to move them into an assisted living facility. I had done my homework on placement options just in case we needed them in the future. Now, the future was staring us in the face. The good news was there was a relatively new assisted living facility only a few miles from their house that was designed like apartments. I had already visited and spoken to some people familiar with the facility. I was well aware that it was going to be expensive, but my parents would have the best of care around the clock, and that was all that mattered.

After a family gathering to explain everything and answer all questions, my two youngest brothers were still not convinced. They were too tied up with denial. At the end of additional exhausting discussions, only my youngest brother remained in denial. He refused to believe the extent of the problem and honestly thought that our parents could remain in their house if everyone would just go by there more frequently. I decided to take a vote on the need for them to move. Everyone, except my youngest brother, was in agreement.

To me, it really didn't matter if everyone agreed with me or not, I was prepared to use my POA to get our parents the level of care they needed. My siblings agreed that I would not have anything repaired or replaced at the house until they were moved. All meals would be brought to them while they were in the house.

We all knew that this was not going to be an easy or quick sell to our mother and father. We decided on a game plan of how we were going to discuss things with them in a united voice. A few days later, we sat down with them to discuss our concerns and what we thought was best for them. My mother was the most vocal as she reeled my father into joining her argument against any changes. They vacillated between "No" and "Maybe," but at the end, they agreed.

My sister and I had gone to visit the facility before we had the conversation with our parents. We agreed that it was nice and offered the level of care they needed. The apartment we chose faced the front of the building and had big windows that allowed a lot of natural light in. This also gave our parents a view of who was coming in and out of the main door to the facility. I knew that we could move some of their furniture into the apartment to make it feel like home. I paid the deposit and secured their space at the facility.

When my sister and I took our parents to visit and meet the staff, they were rather quiet as they toured their proposed new home. They made comments regarding the apartment being small but nice. My mother warmed up to some of the people and even recognized a lady who used to live down the road from their house. Before the visit ended, my mother was a big hit with the administrators and the staff. They had sold my mother on the place, but the verdict was still out for my father. After realizing that some of the men were also World War II veterans, he agreed and accepted the pending move.

Another cooking incident, stripped all shreds of denial away from my youngest brother. He paid our parents a visit the week before their move. He later told me that our mother told him that she had been trying to cook some chicken and dumplings all day and didn't know why the chicken wasn't done. My brother noticed that she had put a frozen chicken in a pot of water and sat it on the stove that was dismantled in the middle of the kitchen floor with the unplugged cord draped across the top. At that point in the story, he openly cried about their condition and clearly saw what I had been talking about for quite a while. With that, all of my siblings were in full agreement that the move to the assisted living facility was a must.

Once the decision was made and a move-in date set, I suffered a bit of an emotional setback. The idea that we were going to uproot and move my parents from their home of more than 60 years made me nauseated and terrified. I knew this was the best decision for them, however, it was not an easy choice. I did not think the hills I was climbing could get any higher or the fall downhill any faster. I had to remind myself to stop screaming and just deal with whatever was coming my way.

I was more emotionally prepared than financially prepared to take on the full responsibility of my parents' care. My parents had been living on a small fixed income. Even with that, I would give them money or buy things from time to time. I had assumed that after I applied their fixed income, the additional cost would be divided among all five siblings. That seemed like a reasonable assumption to me given I had discussed our parents' finances with them. We had all agreed on the care and the placement.

After talking with my siblings about the cost of the assisted living facility and the overall care, I shared with them how much we each needed to contribute each month. Their silence and facial expressions sent my heart straight to my stomach. My body went numb, and my mind went blank as each one explained why she or he didn't have any money or offered "I would if I could." It felt like I had been hit in the face with a brick. The cost of both of my parents' expenses for assisted living had just been dumped squarely in my lap. The unspoken question ... the elephant in the room ... had come to life. I felt as if the buckle of my seat had suddenly popped, and I was being thrown out of the coaster midair.

Angered by my siblings' lack of financial support, I had a long, honest conversation with my husband about what had transpired. He seemed confused by my siblings' response and reminded me that I was not an only child. He gave me his serious medical doctor look as we discussed the options given my parents' physical and mental health. It was clear that they would not live long without the proper level of care and would likely die a tragic unnecessary death given my mother's memory and cognitive functioning.

We both agreed that my parents' care and safety were the most important issues, and we would pay whatever it cost to make sure that they had what they needed. This meant that we had to make some significant lifestyle adjustments and sacrifices to cover all of the expenses. My stress level doubled with the realization that we had four children to care for with each of them having different financial needs. They were either in or entering college or in or graduating from high school. Two of our children, at the time, were enrolled in private, out-of-state, colleges. My husband and I both rolled up our sleeves and worked to do what was necessary to prepare to pay for my parents' care. We no longer talked about or went on vacations. We just looked at each other when major expenses were due and held our collective breaths as we down-scaled our family activities and dipped into our retirement fund and savings account.

While choking with all the expenses, I made one of the toughest financial decisions of my life. I decided to let go of some commercial property that I had paid on for years. That land was part of my retirement plan. This was extremely tough because it always served as a safety net for me. I was not a happy camper, but I was determined to do whatever was necessary for my parents. Thank God for my husband's devotion to my parents and me. Most of all, I thank God for providing us with the financial resources to cover all of our and my parents' expenses.

Intense anger would often surge within me when I listened to my siblings live their lives without feeling the incredible financial burden. Good old C & C continued to be my best friends, and they were with me most of my day. Sometimes, I hid them because I didn't want anyone to know or ask about their presence, and I definitely did not want to share them.

(CAREGIVER'S TIP

Caregiving can become quite expensive depending upon the level of care your loved ones need. A good rule of thumb to help you prepare for financially supporting their care is to plan ahead. Check out resources that are available within your state and at the federal level. Decide what assets can and should be liquidated for your loved ones' care.

Step 5: Identifying a support system(s)

Identifying a strong support system seems like a simple task. Once you are on the roller coaster and have been twisted and turned upside down so many times, you no longer take anything for granted. While people may verbally say, "Just call me if you need me," only a few really will answer your call. Given the lessons I learned from my siblings regarding financial support, I had to redefine support. We all may have our own expectations of support, but support looks different for different people. Therefore, it is necessary to explain to others what you mean and need in terms of support.

Support also comes at different levels. The graph on page 70 illustrates the different levels of support. The inner circle represents core support, the next circle represents mid-level support, and the outer circle represents extended support.

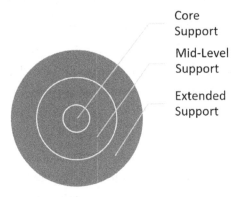

Core
Support

Mid-Level
Support

Extended
Support

The inner core support typically consists of close relatives and dedicated friends and/or paid caregivers. These are the 24/7 "go to" people who are committed to the care plan. Mid-level support consists of people who will do when you ask, but are not consistent. The extended support level also consists of people who will help, but only when it is convenient for them. It is important to identify and write the names and numbers of each person on a corresponding support level. Notate what they agreed to do, as well as, what days it will be done. It is also important that individuals providing support are rotated in order to give the primary caretaker a break.

One of the things I learned is that support comes in different ways and different forms. I also learned not to get upset when it did not come in the form that I needed or wanted. I accepted and realized that these were my parents, and other people were not responsible for them.

Overall, this was the case when it came to financial support. I realized that financially, I was riding alone in the caregiving roller coaster, and it became more frightening each day because I did not see all of the twists coming and had not prepared for this major expense.

The process of getting help

Once you are clear that your loved ones need more help, start the process of determining the level and type of care based on their needs. Remember that care is based on your loved ones' needs, not the convenience or needs of the person responsible for securing the care. Do not wait until there is a crisis, and you must have an emergency placement.

If your loved ones are unable to live independently, but do not need a full time nursing service, you may want to consider an assisted living facility. There are numerous types of placements, therefore, you must do your homework to find the one that best meets your loved ones' needs.

How to find a placement

First step: Make a list of the type of help your loved ones need. Include help needed with ADLs (Activities of Daily Living) and IADLs (Instrumental Activities of Daily Living) as outlined on pages 54 and 55. Decide on the geographical location that would meet their needs. This is important to prevent your loved ones from being totally isolated from family and friends who may visit.

Also, list the amenities that your loved ones would like in order to make the transition easier. Determine the budget and how and who will pay for their care and placement.

Second step: Once you know what type of placement they need, selecting one comes next. The following are ways to help you fulfill this task:

- Word of mouth is one of the best ways to find out about good placements in general and bad ones in particular. This means you must ask friends, family and others if they have placed loved ones; or have known anyone who has a loved one placed in a particular facility; or if any of them have worked at a facility of interest. Try to locate the family members of residents in the recommended placement and ask them about their experience. Similarly, talk to employees and ask questions about their experience at the facility. One of the main questions should be: "Would you put your loved ones here?"
- Ask for recommendations from your loved ones' doctors and any medical facility into which they have been admitted. It is important to seek the advice of the medical facility's nursing staff as to reputable placements that would meet your loved ones' needs.
- Contact your state agency for aging for recommendations. Also, you can do an online search for more information on placements. Go to www.eldercare.gov, a federal resource site, to find your nearest agency on aging for assistance.

- Contact the government office that investigates long-term care facility complaints in your loved ones' state of residence. This office advocates for residents and their families and can help you find the latest health inspection reports on specific assisted living or long-term care nursing facilities. More importantly, these reports can tell you which facilities have had complaints or other serious problems.

Third step: Generate a list of the top facilities that meet your loved ones' needs.

- Plan a visit to interview and tour the facilities. Write down all of your questions so that you do not forget any. Some of the questions that you should ask include:
  - What is the range of care or assistance the facility provides?
  - What are the facility's procedures and policies for residents?
  - How frequently does the facility communicate with family regarding their loved ones?
  - What is the visitation policy?
  - What are the qualification levels of your staff?
  - What is the staff to resident ratio?
  - What is the turnover rate of your staff providing direct care to residents?
  - What is the cost?
  - Are there any financial assistance plans with other agencies (e.g., Veterans Administration) or

supplemental funding programs (e.g., Medicaid) or are all costs out-of-pocket?

- Ask for an application packet and a contract to review before you decide definitely on the placement.

- When you visit, ask yourself the following:
    - Does the place look welcoming?
    - Is it clean?
    - Does it have an offensive odor?
    - Are the staff members friendly?
    - Do the residents look clean and well kept?
    - How spontaneous is the staff with the residents?
    - Are the facility grounds well kept?
    - Were my questions answered fully?
    - Would the space and amenities meet my loved ones' needs?

- Make sure you arrange to take your loved ones for a visit and make sure that they ask all of the questions they need to.

- For the top two or three facilities, drop in unannounced at different times and different days to assess the placement. Talk with family members of residents that may be visiting.

Most assisted living facilities do not have any financial assistance. Payments are expected each month, and your loved ones will be evicted for nonpayment. Veterans and their spouses may be eligible for VA benefits that can offset some of the cost of their care.

All assisted living facilities or nursing homes are not created equal. Therefore, it is very important to do your homework. Services may be similar, but the quality may vary greatly. Some services at a typical assisted living facility include:

- Three meals a day served in a common dining area
- Snacks and juices
- Assistance with eating, bathing, dressing
- Housekeeping services
- Transportation for activities
- Access to nursing services
- Round-the-clock security
- Emergency call systems in each resident's living space
- Exercise and wellness programs
- Medication management
- Laundry services
- Social and recreational activities

Do not think for one minute that you can simply walk away once your loved ones are placed in a care facility. This is absolutely not the case. They will still need you for support, and the facility will be looking for you to make decisions on their behalf. You must be willing to visit and call on a frequent basis to assure that your loved ones are getting the best of care and treatment. Placement is only part of the ongoing roller coaster ride.

Emotional Survival Tip for the Recognition Phase

Stress became a way of life, and I often had to find a peaceful place to sit and relax ... clear my mind ... breathe ... pray and meditate. My favorite peaceful place was on the shores of Old Hickory Lake near my parents' home where I could release the stress of the day. Studies have shown that our physical and emotional health can be negatively impacted by stress. High levels of stress can contribute to high blood pressure and increase the risk factors for heart disease. Stress may also result in anxiety and depression. Our typical response to stress, which is to ignore it, can also result in a compromised immune system, which can make the body more susceptible to colds and other illnesses.

While we cannot always avoid stressful situations, we can change our response to them by developing a *relaxation response*. The relaxation response is a state of deep rest that can be achieved by techniques including deep breathing, mindfulness meditation, yoga and progressive muscle relaxation. Prayer is also a key component for relaxation for many people.

Techniques to try:

- **Deep Breathing** - Take time to slow your breath, be aware of it, feel it moving completely in and completely out of your lungs. Inhale through your nose and exhale through your mouth.

- **Mindfulness Meditation** - This practice involves sitting comfortably, focusing on your breathing, and bringing your mind's attention to the present moment without drifting into concerns about the past or the future.
- **Yoga** - This practice typically emphasizes physical postures to stretch the limbs and muscles, breathing techniques and meditation to calm the mind.
- **Progressive Muscle Relaxation**- In this relaxation technique, you focus on slowly tensing and then relaxing each muscle group.

CAREGIVER'S TIP

Practice controlled slow breathing. When you breathe six (6) breaths a minute, your breath becomes aligned with the rhythm of your heart, and this is good for cardiovascular health.

PHASE 2

The Reality Phase – Caregiving
Decisions ... Decisions ... Decisions

Chapter 4

The Reality of the Reality Phase

A S I REFLECT back, I thought things were smooth and under control when I entered the Reality Phase. It really took me by surprise because I was calm, and the bright sun was beaming down on the back of my neck, and a warm breeze was hitting my face from the fresh air as the roller coaster entered the long climb to the Reality Phase. I thought I had become used to all of the ups and downs, as well as the twists and turns of the ride. I had even adjusted to the jostling and the loud noise of the track. At least, so I thought.

I couldn't figure it out, but this climb appeared different from others. I actually had begun to get comfortable. I had survived the Recognition Phase and was rather proud of myself as I thought about all that I had managed to accomplish and prepare for. I closed my eyes for a moment and enjoyed the bright sun and the warm breeze. I even gloated to myself about things finally being under control. When I opened my eyes and looked around, reality hit me in the face. I was sitting 350 feet in the air on the very top of the roller coaster with a straight downhill drop at 60 miles per hour before me. Oh no! I said my prayers and grabbed C & C as quickly as I could. This roller coaster ride was truly keeping my prayer and meditation life active and alive.

The **Reality Phase** starts long after the roller coaster ride has pulled out of the gate. This is when the actual full-time *Caregiving* starts.

After years of working with clients as a psychologist to help them develop effective coping skills, I found myself struggling beyond words at times. My well-honed coping skills were missing in action—MIA, as it were. I was relegated to existing on a day-to-day basis. To complicate matters, I had begun to question and review each decision I had already made one by one. The constant second-guessing only served to make me feel unsure and unsteady. Questions were thrown at me from all directions. People were expecting quick responses. And I couldn't get past the questions in my head: Is this the best thing for them? How will they adjust? How do I respond to the not-so-veiled unflattering comments and judgmental attitudes from family and friends?

It is a cultural practice in the African American community that you do not leave your loved ones for someone else to take care of. Could or should my sister or I possibly move in with them or have them move in with either of our families? Would it make sense to give up our jobs and careers?

I felt judged by others for the decisions that I had to make. I know that physically I was not alone, but mentally, I was in a desert by myself. Although my husband was super supportive, at times, I felt that he had the luxury of ignoring the resistance and misplaced anger from my parents, while all I could do was grin and bear it. Yes, your loved ones can change from the loving persons you may have known to the aggressive combative persons you don't know or even like. I would have loved it if my parents could have lived their lives out independently in their own home. However, that was not the case. Decisions had to be made, and they had charged me with making the necessary decisions for their care.

CAREGIVER'S TIP

As the caregiver and primary decision maker, you must be able to look at matters objectively, as well as with compassion. Therefore, while everyone may not agree with your choices, your primary obligation is to make sure that those choices are in the best interest of your loved ones.

Reality brings out old friends and bad habits ...

While I was grinning and bearing up through my parents' personality changes and my own feelings of helplessness, my old road dogs, C & C, were there to help ease my pain and help me cope with disappointment and self-pity. Then, one day, I remembered another old friend, "LPC," better known as Lay's Potato Chips. LPC and I knew each other from way back when, and we used to hang out during stressful times before I started this ride. It didn't take long for us to pick up right where we had left off. In fact, LPC was happy to see that C & C were already in the seat with me. We became an inseparable foursome. You rarely saw me without them nearby.

My husband had become concerned and even made some comments about leaving them alone or at least not having them around all the time. He didn't think our relationship was healthy. He had no idea how much they helped me with the tension I felt most of the time.

After his frequent comments about them, I noticed that I really didn't want to do anything without them. I actually needed them and kept them close at hand and even requested them when I did public events as part of my contract rider.

Over time, I noticed that I had gained weight and that the sodium intake from my friends had elevated my blood pressure and left me feeling tired and bloated. We were together so often that I finally had to put some limits and rules in place. My new rule was that I could no longer see them before 10:00 a.m. That rule was harder to enforce than you would think, but I did it, for the most part.

CAREGIVER'S TIP

There is only one you. Maintaining your own health is essential to living a fulfilling life. You cannot truly help others if you cannot help yourself. Self-care must be your first care.

Chapter 5

Self-Care ... Who Me?

I T WAS DURING the Reality Phase that I realized that all of my plans for my parents' care did not include any thought of my own care. *I was burning the candle at both ends, and it was bending in the middle!* I became so busy that my days seemed to blend together. As the climbs continued to get higher, the only thing I could do was pray and hold onto C & C and LPC. They were there when others were not around and often replaced even my favorite unhealthy fast food junk meals. My love for them was reflected in my significant weight gain. I rarely ate healthy, well-balanced meals anymore. My family became accustomed to take-outs and one-pot dishes like chicken casseroles. I ate many of my meals in my car as I rushed from place to place. With my weight gain and high blood pressure, other ailments emerged. This was one more thing I was not prepared to deal with.

One day, I looked in the mirror, and I wanted to cry. Underneath my makeup and smile were dark blemishes and scars on my face from adult acne, and dark circles and bags under my eyes that refused to leave. My self-care was long gone.

I was significantly overweight with frequent headaches, back and neck pain and chronic stomachaches. I chewed Tums like chewing gum. Most of my stress was definitely felt in my stomach. I was extremely tired and irritable most days, and it showed in my body.

The only thing I knew to do or thought I could do was push ahead. Even when support was available, I had the unending weight of having POA for both parents. I honestly felt like the decisions I made for them could result in life or death. This conviction created and sustained my endless anxiety.

In addition to dealing with my parents, I still had a husband and children, as well as a business to run. My husband constantly encouraged me to take better care of myself and let some of my responsibilities go. He frequently cautioned me that if I continued "going" at such a frantic pace, then I would get really sick. Then, he would listen patiently as I explained why I could not stop or slow down. I would tell him that I did not have time to get sick. My responsibilities and, most of all, my love for my parents would not allow me to slow down. My husband clearly understood my dilemma, yet, he continued to remind me about my health. Of course, I didn't listen to him, as I lost control of my weight and overall self-care.

The roller coaster ride was not only costing me a great deal emotionally and financially, but also physically. I did not know how to change things, but each day, I managed to put on the mask, make up, fashionable attire, a big smile and an "I'm every woman" demeanor for the public. I convinced myself that I could not dare share how I was truly feeling because I was the strong one.

Chapter 6

Plans vs. Decisions

URING THE REALITY Phase, I learned that plans are just that, plans! In life, situations can and will change without warning. Flexibility is a must regardless of how solid the plan. It's one thing to develop a plan, but it is a completely different venture when others are involved in carrying it out. It quickly becomes complex when you are depending on others. My parents' care plan was in place, and all my siblings and I had to do was execute it. With a few bumpy tracks, the care plan was put into motion. At times, the mere thought of the care plan brought tears of sadness.

After additional conversations with my siblings about the cost of care, it became apparent that their help would come in the form of hands on tasks for our parents. That help was priceless for keeping our parents' appointments and ensuring that life was in order at their place. My husband and I accepted the financial responsibility and made tough decisions. Some of the decisions were emotional and quite painful due to their outcome, like seeing our retirement income deplete. However, we were in total agreement that we would make the necessary sacrifices for my parents to have the best of care and quality of life.

Chapter 7

Moving Day

THE CLIMB TO Reality was long and arduous. I approached my parents' moving day with a sense of anticipation coupled with rumblings of uncertainty. However, I definitely had not anticipated my mother calling the police that morning to request that they arrest all of her children. That was a sharp curve with a big drop. Once my siblings and I regrouped from our mother's opening act, we were able to laugh and refocus on the main event–moving our parents out of their home of more than 60 years.

Prior to moving day, my siblings and I tried to prepare our parents for their relocation as best we could. I warned my siblings that whatever we were feeling, we all had to have the same positive upbeat game face when we talked about their move. During our conversations with them, I reminded our parents of how many fun activities and outings they would be participating in at the assisted living facility. We all talked about how nice it was going to be to have almost anything they wanted at their fingertips.

My mother's facial expressions and the rolling of her eyes were clear indications that she did not buy it at all. She quickly and sarcastically reminded me that she didn't need or want anyone cooking or cleaning for them and proudly stated that she had been doing things just fine by herself for over 80 years. My father simply gave his usual nod of agreement. I smiled in agreement as I continued to try and convince them that it was time to let others do for them while they relaxed. I also reminded them that they would be close enough to their house that neighbors and church members could drop by anytime to visit, and they could continue to attend church. My mother half-heartedly accepted this notion, while my father remained silent.

On moving day, Mr. and Mrs. T. arrived on time to take our parents out for the entire day while my siblings and I moved their belongings. Once they were gone, we jumped into action working nonstop to move them to the assisted living facility. My sister and a few of her friends had already conducted a deep cleaning of our parents' new place. Of course, the place was already clean, but we are like many other folks–it's not clean until we have cleaned. Thankfully, my sister had already taken some of our parents' clothes and other essentials to their new apartment.

I wanted their new home to be as comfortable and welcoming as I could make it. For years, my mother had complained about their bedroom furniture being old. So, I surprised them by buying them a brand new bedroom suite.

We picked out pieces of their favorite furniture to move into the new place. Picking out which pieces of their lives to take with them and which to leave behind left us emotionally drained. My siblings and I were crying one moment and laughing and being silly the next. As painful as it was, we all knew it was for the best.

We worked all day to make sure that when our parents walked into their new place it would say "Welcome home." Every box was unpacked and every item was in its place. My sister created a gorgeous floral wreath for their front door. The beautiful spring colors of yellow, pink, purple and white were so brilliant that everyone was tempted to touch the flowers to see if they were real. When you entered the apartment, a blue and yellow color theme welcomed you and radiated warmth and serenity. Our parents' mahogany drop-leaf dining room table was in the kitchenette and partially covered by one of my mother's vintage white tablecloths trimmed in lace. A floral centerpiece accented with blue and yellow rested in the center of the table.

The kitchenette was fully stocked with their favorite snacks and drinks. Family pictures adorned the walls. Shower curtains and accent towels decorated the bathroom. A quilted, sky blue bedspread covered their new queen-sized bed. Bright blue and yellow pillows added a finishing accent to the living room couch. Our parents' favorite matching recliners took up residence near the large front windows. More family pictures of priceless memories rested on a pair of end tables and filled both sides of the TV cabinet. The place looked absolutely beautiful–bright and new, yet, homey and welcoming.

In our desire to make everything perfect for our parents' arrival, preparing their apartment took longer than we anticipated. It was late in the afternoon before we were finished. That being so, we thought it would be best to have them stay one last night in their house and have them to come to their new apartment the next day in time for lunch. The staff at the facility also thought it was a great idea and planned to introduce them to the other residents. And, my brothers agreed to bring our parents' pastor with them on the next day. Truth be told, my sister and I were glad for the delay because we were exhausted.

When I awoke the next morning, the cloudy and overcast sky matched my gloomy mood. The day had finally arrived. My parents were going to physically leave their home. Moving residences can be a challenge at any age. Moving two octogenarians from the only home they had known as adults was nerve-wracking. Without question, my parents did not want to move and still did not fully comprehend why they were being moved.

My sister and I got up bright and early to go over to our parents' new home. We walked through and took an inventory of what had been done. We didn't want to miss anything and wanted to make sure they had everything they needed. We jotted down a list of odds and ends that we had forgotten and decided to run to the store. As the time ticked by, both of our moods continued to match the dark overcast sky. While in the store, we heard a loud noise that sounded as if someone was working on the roof of the building.

We looked at each other and asked, "What in the world is that noise?"

Nevertheless, we continued to shop without giving the noise much more thought. We should have realized that something was wrong because there were only a few people in the entire store. When we approached the front of the store to check out, we overheard other customers talking about the rain. The sky had opened up and buckets of rain were steadily pouring down. The loud noise that we heard earlier was rain, and it was not easing up. The parking lot had already flooded. After deciding to run for the car, we discovered that the water was well above our ankles. It was unbelievable how much rain had come down in such a short period of time. We wasted money buying an umbrella because it did absolutely no good. The wind was blowing so hard that the rain was coming down at an angle. Once we were safely in our car, we called our bothers for an update on our parents. They were with them and their pastor waiting for the rain to ease up before leaving.

Our parents finally arrived several hours later with their coats dripping with water and looking like two wet lost puppies. My sister and I rushed to take their wet coats and hats. They slowly entered their new apartment—new home–seemingly on tiptoe and looked around with a look of curiosity on their faces. Their pastor talked about how pretty and nice everything looked, but my mother's face suggested that she did not want to hear a sales pitch about the place. After my sister and I showed them around their new place, our parents politely agreed that it was nice and seemed to relax as they recognized some of their familiar belongings. Soon, different staff members stopped in to introduce themselves. The staff members were friendly and tried hard to make them feel at home. As the staff escorted them to the dining room for lunch, they introduced them to other residents.

My siblings and I decided to leave but assured our parents that we would be back later in the evening. As I walked out, I cried as hard as the rain that was still coming down. Through my tears, I noticed that my sister and brothers were doing the same.

When we returned that evening, my parents happily introduced us to people they had already met. We brought a pizza and their favorite milk shakes and sat around their apartment laughing and talking. Several of their grandchildren came over and jumped on them with plenty of hugs and kisses. The smell of food, the background noise of the TV, the chatter and laughter from numerous conversations quickly brought life to their new home. As the evening turned to night, a nurse came by and gave them their medication. Not long afterwards, our parents politely put us out. My mother jokingly said that she might as well check out her new bed and that we needed to go home. On that note, we cleaned up our mess and left—exhausted and grateful.

Didn't it rain, children, children? Didn't it rain? The hard rain continued throughout the night. It was the strangest rain I had ever seen. My siblings and I had been so preoccupied with the move that we had not bothered to listen to the news or any kind of weather report. We had no idea that one of the most eventful days in our family's history would be accompanied by the worst flooding in more than 30 years.

(CAREGIVER'S TIP

Be sure to explain fully to your loved ones why they are moving. Introduce them to their new place and get their buy-in before you move them. Make sure that you decorate their "new home" with familiar pictures and family keepsakes, if at all possible.

Chapter 8

The Adjustment

AFTER SEVERAL MONTHS, my parents seemed to have settled into their new environment. Other than my mother complaining about the lack of flavor in the food or my father not caring to engage in social gatherings with other residents, they did not voice many complaints. Regarding the food, my mother's favorite comment was "Our folks were not cooking the food today."

It was her way of conveying that the assisted living facility had no African American cooks, and the food was somewhat bland. On the other hand, my parents loved my multiflavored pound cake, and I would bring them some whenever I baked one. Being aware of their elevated blood sugar levels, I sliced the cake very thin on one visit. In order to limit them eating too much cake later in the evening, I offered some of the cake to the staff.

My mother looked at the slice that I had cut for her and held it up to her face and said "James do you see this? This slice is so thin that I can read the newspaper through it!"

I could only laugh as she laughed and continued to tease me about the thin slice of cake.

When she noticed that I was offering the staff members some cake, she made a funny facial expression and quickly added "James, who brings you cake and then gives it away?"

Once again, I could only laugh.

To be expected, my mother, being the social butterfly that she was, had a much easier adjustment than my father. She made new friends and engaged in many of the activities. However, her wardrobe posed a particular issue. One of the greatest challenges my sister and I faced with my mother was getting her to wear pants. My mother had never worn pants a day in her life and had refused to consider the idea. Our problem was that she needed to wear pants or sweatpants given the activities in the facility. My sister and I debated about how we could get her to wear pants and who was going to talk with her about it. We decided that I would buy my mother a nice heavy warm-up suit and sneakers, and my sister would be responsible for getting her to wear them.

I bought her a fashionable pink, soft, warm-up suit with sparkling designs on the jacket and white and pink sneakers to match. I knew my mother would love the colors and the "bling bling," but it was going to be a hard sell to convince her to put her legs in pants. I smiled and told my sister "Good luck!"

I must give it to my sister, she got our mother to wear the warm-up suit on an outing. My sister and the staff were so excited when she finally wore the outfit. She looked fantastic, but my mother remained quiet while enjoying all of the compliments she received. Once she returned from the outing, my sister asked her how she liked wearing pants. Her response was epic! My mother told my sister, without cracking a smile, that she guessed she liked the pants because "at least they kept my "pu**y" warm!" When my sister told me what our mother had said, I was totally speechless–but we laughed uncontrollably!

My father was never a fan of his new home, but accepted it as long as my mother was around. He was quiet and somewhat guarded when others tried to engage him in conversations or befriend him. My parents were the only African American couple in the facility. I had no idea that my father had major unresolved feelings and issues related to race, especially about racial conditions in the South.

At one point, my father became concerned that one of the white male residents liked my mother a little too much. He mentioned that the man was "real friendly" when my mother was with him. My father started taking his cane with him everywhere and stated that he would knock the guy in the head if he kept on looking the wrong way at my mother. My brothers came to the rescue, spoke with our father and reassured him that he did not need to use his cane.

At least one of my siblings, as well as my niece and her children visited them daily. I visited as frequently as I could and called them daily. My husband often spoke to the nurse or other medical personnel to troubleshoot medical issues. I made a point of dropping in to visit at odd times of the day or night. I also encouraged my siblings to do the same.

There were friends and families with my parents almost daily. My parents adored their grandchildren and, most of all, their great-grandchildren. Their faces would light up anytime they saw them coming. The fact that they were in a new place did not stop their great-grandchildren from playing and climbing up on them and asking a hundred questions. The great-grandchildren were also a favorite with the staff and residents. They talked to everyone and met no strangers. My parents loved every moment they had with them.

CAREGIVER'S TIP

When staff at facilities see loved ones visiting frequently and at irregular times, the care is likely to be better. Make sure family and friends do "pop-up" visits at odd times on a weekly basis.

CAREGIVER'S TIP

If it is safe and possible, bring children and grandchildren to visit your loved ones, especially if there is a close bond between them. Explain the changes in your loved ones to the children before their visit.

The roller coaster ride had become somewhat bearable. We had made it to a new phase, and I was still buckled in and holding on tight. Transitions are hard for most people, especially for older people, and my parents were no exception. In addition to the emotional aspect of their transition to the assisted living facility, my sister and I soon discovered the challenge of the practical aspect of managing simple things, such as keeping track of their clothing or their appointments and other activities.

We learned that we needed to label our parents' clothing and other belongings. Too often their things would be lost or misplaced. My sister and I, along with a friend, spent hours one day writing their names on all their possessions. In the end, my sister decided it would be easier if she washed and put up their clothing herself.

During the first few years of their residence, my parents were not confined to the facility. They attended their church and other events in the community. We often took them to family gatherings and did other activities with them. Despite this, the aging process continued to take a toll on them. Their physical health declined, and my mother's memory deteriorated at an accelerated pace. When they were no longer physically able to leave the facility for outings, we all crammed into their apartment and brought tons of food and gifts for holidays and birthdays. There were so many people and so much laughter that the staff and other residents would come by to join in on the activities and fun. My parents enjoyed those times as we ate, laughed and talked. It was as close as possible to old times. My siblings and I did not miss an opportunity to gather and celebrate. These gatherings continued for years.

One day when my sister arrived for her usual visit, she noticed an ambulance outside with the lights on. To her surprise, it was for our father who had become incoherent and nonresponsive. My mother was in a panic, but the medics had reassured her that her husband would be all right. When I received a call from my sister, I left Atlanta immediately for Nashville's TriStar Summit Hospital. My husband called the hospital's emergency room to check on my father's medical status. Apparently, my father had become dehydrated which caused the confusion and other cognitive deficiencies. He was admitted for a few days for additional testing. My mother was updated about his condition and taken to the hospital to visit him.

When I arrived in Nashville, I went straight to the hospital to see my father, and then, I went to visit my mother. I explained to her what had happened to him and that he should be released to come home in a few days. All of a sudden, my mother began to cry. Through her sobs, she kept asking why no one had told her that my father was in the hospital. I sat there, baffled by what I was hearing. I gently reminded her that she had visited him at the hospital earlier that day, and that she was with him in the apartment when the ambulance arrived.

Nevertheless, she kept stating, "No one told me a thing!" and insisted that she had not been informed. My attempts to convince her otherwise were totally unsuccessful and futile.

When I left her that afternoon, I fought back tears of helplessness as I realized the extent of my mother's cognitive decline. I shared this information with my siblings to help brace them for what was to come. The roller coaster ride of caregiving had become even more unpredictable with shorter drops and sharper curves and twists.

The staff spent extra time to engage and preoccupy my mother so that she would not worry about my father. They repeatedly reassured her that he would return in a few days. My mother seemed fine when she went to bed alone for the first time since being in the facility. However, she awoke in the middle of the night. And when she could not find my father, she called 911 in a panic. Because she was calling from their private phone in their apartment, the police responded. My mother was determined to file a missing persons report and have the police search for my father. The staff and the police spent considerable time explaining that my father was in the hospital. In the end, her nurse had to administer medication to calm her down and help her sleep that night.

My father indeed returned to the apartment in a few days appearing quite healthy. After my mother began calling 911 anytime she could not locate my father, we had to remove their private phone. Of course, neither one of them was happy with that decision. My mother objected in a very defiant tone when I explained the problem.

She argued, "What is the use of paying taxes, if I can't call them? They work for us. We pay their salary, and I needed them!"

In response, I simply smiled and fought the urge to laugh out loud.

CAREGIVER'S TIP

It may become necessary for you to remove your loved ones' easy access to devices such as telephones and car keys for their own safety. Make sure that you have a viable alternative in place to ensure that they can communicate with emergency services, if necessary.

Chapter 9

The Downhill Plunge

AS THE MONTHS and years passed, my parents' health continued to decline. The roller coaster ride had shifted from me being terrified of the speed and the twists and turns to sheer fear of my parents' death. Even so, there were days filled with laughter and days filled with tears. My mother used her strong social skills and humor to play things off as long as she could. It was unclear at times if she truly recognized my siblings or me. That did not stop her from talking as if everything was fine. My father, who was usually quiet, became more assertive as he aged. Both of my parents began to have difficulty with mobility. My father became more feeble and developed Kyphosis or what is commonly known as a humped back. My mother often complained about her legs hurting and had difficulty walking. As a result, they became confined to the assisted living facility and their level of care was increased. Hospitalizations were more frequent. Each time my phone rang with a call from Tennessee, I held my breath, and my heart thudded against my rib cage. The proliferation of emergency calls requiring medical attention drew me closer to my friends, C & C and LPC.

The decisions became harder to make because the consequences became greater. I knew that my parents' decline was imminent. Each time I visited them, there was a marked change in their behavior. Rather than jokes and laughter when I entered their apartment, I was usually met by silence. They both tended to fall asleep in their recliners with the TV serving as background noise. When I would speak and call their names, it took several minutes for them to become aware of my presence. Their faces reflected tiredness from the aging process more than that of illness. It was extremely difficult to watch my parents fading away in front of me. I was back and forth to Nashville so often, I considered opening a psychological practice there.

Emotional Survival Tips for The Reality Phase

- Understand and accept what is and isn't in your control.
- Do not take everything as a personal act against you. Your loved ones' abrasive attitudes and manners are not a reflection of your love and care.
- Be flexible.
- Allow yourself time to grieve all the changes.
- Be patient with your loved ones, they are dealing with more than you.
- Stop and take time for self-care.

CAREGIVER'S TIP

When your loved ones become difficult to deal with, remember: They are not intentionally giving you a hard time. They are having a hard time!

PHASE 3

The Release Phase - Post-Caregiving
Release comes in phases … as you will discover

Chapter 10

Preparing to Let Go

AFTER SO MANY years on the caregiving roller coaster, it dawned on me that the ride may really come to an end one day. While that was what I prayed for, the reality of what that would really mean was emotionally devastating. Living and functioning through fear and anxiety had become a way of life. The idea of an abrupt end only increased my anxiety and tripled my need for my "ride or die" friends C & C and LPC.

After about five years in the assisted living facility, my parents were no longer fully ambulatory. They needed a higher level of care given their limited mobility. The reality of this was overwhelming on many levels. The assisted living facility had provided excellent care and met all of their needs up to this point. Typically, the next logical step in the progression of care would be a skilled nursing home facility.

Both of my parents definitely met the criteria for admission. However, I did not have the heart to entertain the idea.

Besides, I had heard my mother repeatedly say down through the years that she never wanted to be placed in a nursing home. In fact, she had asked me personally not to allow anyone to "stick" her in a nursing home. And knowing my mother's strong objection, I made arrangements to honor her request.

The further decline in my parents' health presented another steep climb with a sharp drop. I dreaded the idea of finding a new location and moving my two ailing parents. I discussed with my siblings our parents' need for a higher level of care and the challenges of finding an appropriate placement. I made it clear that a nursing home was ruled out as a first option and would only be considered as the very last resort.

During my search for another placement, Mr. and Mrs. T., who had helped care for my parents before moving into the assisted living facility, informed me that they had a personal care home at their private residence. They told me that they had the ability to provide one-on-one service. I was excited because that would meet my parents' needs and be a great alternative to a nursing home. Mrs. T. shared her work history and experience with me *and* that she had a degree in nursing. She also explained her staff's work experience and schedule. I was even able to meet one of her staff members. I collected references and spoke directly with the daughter of a woman she had cared for until her death.

In my search for a placement, I also discovered that my parents qualified for in-home nursing services to assist with their care. This would mean that Mrs. T. would have outside help, as well. I was both relieved and excited as I reported the information to my siblings. We decided that this should work well, given our parents' familiarity and past experience with Mr. and Mrs. T.

With the decision made, we proceeded to plan and arrange the move. Leaving the assisted living facility was almost as hard as leaving their home five years before. This time there were no questions or resistance from my parents. They seemed oblivious to what was happening although they had been informed. The day they left the assisted living facility, the staff and other residents came by to wish them well and say "Goodbye." The slow, silent walk from their apartment to the main door felt like a funeral procession as residents looked on in silence or made farewell comments. The only thing missing was the music and the pastor walking ahead of us reading scripture from a Bible. My mother and father held tight to their walkers as they took slow, careful steps. My mother appeared tearful as it seemed to dawn on her that they would not be returning after numerous "Good-byes" and verbal expressions of how they would be missed. My father appeared to look puzzled, but managed to hold his chin high. My sister and I could not hold back the tears as we looked at our parents' faces. We made it to the car with water-filled eyes and wet faces.

My parents initially appeared to adjust fairly well to their move. The fact that they were further away from their friends and community was a real drawback. This made it difficult for others to drop by for visits. However, my siblings and I made frequent visits to our parents' new setting.

With each visit, I noticed that they were less alert and more lethargic. While this was somewhat expected, it was hard to observe. I became concerned with their placement after the first month when I was informed that my parents were going to be placed in respite care while Mr. and Mrs. T. went on a two-week vacation.

"Vacation? Respite care!" I thought wildly.

No one had mentioned or discussed the possibility of this happening. My parents had not been there two months, and they were leaving for a vacation. Where was her staff? I was angry and thrown off balance. However, I felt helpless to complain or express my true feelings too much because my parents' care was in their hands. When I mentioned my concern, I was told this vacation had been planned months ago. I thought it would have been nice if they had told me. I had not consented to a respite placement, but what choice did I have?

My concerns continued to grow as my parents' health seemed to rapidly decline. After about four months with Mr. and Mrs. T., my father required hospitalization and a placement in rehabilitation. During a visit, I discovered that my mother had developed a deep awful looking sore on the bottom of her left foot. This was not just a little sore but one that was about the size of a fifty-cent piece. It was clearly infected and needed a special wound care nurse for treatment. When I asked Mrs. T. about it, she casually noted that she put an over-the-counter cream on it. I was extremely stressed because I was the only person who recognized the seriousness of the sore. I took pictures of the wound and sent them to my husband who confirmed that immediate medical attention was needed. He indicated that it was a stage three ulcer which meant the sore was down to the muscle in her foot. In my efforts to get her the needed care, the situation escalated to a verbal altercation with the in-home nursing service before a wound care nurse was provided. I was livid, and I did not bite my tongue when expressing my feelings. My mind reeled with questions: Why had no one noticed the wound? What would have happened if I had not discovered it? Where was Mrs. T.'s staff each time I came for a visit?

When I made inquiries, Mr. and Mrs. T. deflected with soliloquies of how much work my parents required for their care. This really angered me because I paid them what they charged, plus my parents had additional home care nursing services. I could sense their increased tension and defensiveness as I asked more questions. My parents could no longer speak for themselves, and I had to be their voice and inquire more. The more concerned I became, the more I made unannounced "pop up" visits.

One night, I arrived about 9:00 p.m. My parents were in bed, but my mother was awake. As I sat by her bed, she complained about her legs hurting and being hungry. When I asked Mrs. T. about my mother being hungry, I was told that she had eaten earlier and could not be hungry. I insisted that she be given some more food while I was there. I was appalled by what was brought to her to eat. It looked like a hodge-podge of leftovers from different meals. I knew my mother was really hungry as I watched her quickly eat every bite of food on the plate. For me, that was a clear sign that something was not adding up. I rubbed my mother's legs that night to ease her pain. She tearfully and repeatedly thanked me for the visit. I stayed until she dropped off to sleep. I left feeling heavy-hearted and bereft of words. I knew something had to be done now. I loved my parents way too much to entertain them not getting the best of care.

The next day, I wrote Mrs. T. a letter expressing my concerns about my parents' lack of adequate care. Shortly after that, I was informed that Mrs. T. injured her back caring for my parents and needed to place them in respite, once again. This was the last straw for me. I was in sheer panic mode, but I knew that my parents would not be going back to Mr. and Mrs. T's home. The roller coaster ride had taken a loop-the-loop and left me hanging upside down.

CAREGIVER'S TIP

If you are considering a private residential setting, make sure they are licensed and qualified to provide services. Do the same homework you would do for an assisted living facility and/or a nursing home.

Chapter 11

The Process of Letting Go

THIS PROCESS CAN be emotionally paralyzing. I wanted to make sure in my heart of hearts that I had done everything humanly possible to provide my parents with the best of care to the very end. Before my parents were sent to respite care, I spoke with my siblings about my decision that our parents could not return to Mr. and Mrs. T's care. Out of respect for my mother's wish not to be placed in a nursing home, I decided that they would return to their own home of more than 60 years to live out their final days. I believed that it would be the best way to honor them.

Once my decision was made, I created a list of actions that needed to be put into first gear right away. The list consisted of the following:

- Find the absolutely best full-time home nursing staff for my parents. This was not an easy task. I called and interviewed countless candidates. I finally chose someone highly-qualified with years of experience and excellent communication skills. My parents responded well to the candidate, also. And as things go in small towns, the candidate even knew one of my brothers from years ago.

- Obtain a current update from everyone providing care before the transition. This gave me a clear picture of what had been done and what would be needed. I had to decide who would no longer be needed in the new care plan and eliminate them.

- Hire a contractor to make the necessary structural changes in the house in order to be compliant with the disabled persons and health care guidelines. Among other things, doorways had to be widened to accommodate wheelchairs; the bathroom tub had to be removed and a walk-in shower built; rails had to be affixed to various areas; and hardwood flooring had to be installed throughout my parents' home.

- Reorganize the support team. I clearly knew that everyone who volunteered to help would not necessarily provide the type of support my parents needed. I met with my siblings and worked out a schedule for added night coverage before our parents returned.

Once the remodeling was completed, my siblings and I worked diligently to get our parents' house in order. Upon our parents' discharge from respite, they were to be transferred to their own home under my care. I was excited and terrified at the same time.

Bright ideas and good intentions …

My sister and I had the bright idea that once our parents returned home Saturday morning, we would take care of them over the weekend by ourselves and have the nursing service start the following Monday. We thought that this would give them time to get readjusted to being back in their own house. We had decorated the house with bright colors just like we thought they would love. We bought or baked their favorite things to eat. We even decided to have a big welcome home Sunday cookout with family and friends.

We spent Friday excitedly calling and inviting everyone. We knew that our parents loved entertaining others, and we thought it would be like old times except we would be doing all the work. It all sounded like fun and a good idea, right? Wrong! We were not prepared or equipped to care for our parents for a day much less an entire weekend!

Their last return home …

My parents arrived from the respite center in two shiny ambulances. The medic team brought them in on stretchers and deposited them, rather unceremoniously, into the family room like so many packages. At the same time, one of the drivers handed us two bags of medication and asked,

"Where do you want them?" My sister and I weren't sure if he meant our parents or the bags of medication.

Our mother rescued us from our awkward moment of confusion by stating that she was tired. It was perfect timing on her part. In response, the medics carried our parents into their bedroom and laid them in their beds.

While our mother and father took a nap, my sister and I prepared lunch and tried to sort out all of their medications. We had no idea that they were on so many different medications that needed to be administered at various times throughout the day. Some pills were once a day, some twice and others three times a day. Then, some were to be taken in the morning, some at lunch and others at night only.

My sister and I just looked at each other as she sorted my father's medications, and I sorted my mother's. We had bottles of pills all over the table and had not determined the best location to house them. By the time we figured out which pills needed to be taken at lunch, our parents were awake and ready to eat. We decided to carry lunch to them because the kitchen table was covered with bottles and bottles of pills. Before they could eat, however, we discovered that they required diapering. My sister and I cleaned them up and changed their protective undergarments. This was neither a fun nor an easy task, but we completed it.

After lunch, we managed to get our parents into their wheelchairs and rolled them into the family room. I was amazed that neither of them mentioned being back in their home or the changes that had been made. It became apparent to me that they did not recognize the house.

Nevertheless, I still expected them to talk about how happy they were to be back home. They looked around and commented, every now and then, on things they liked without any real sense that this was their home and their things. My parents seemed to have déjà vu moments as they became oriented to the house. I felt disappointed and an overwhelming sense of sadness. Intellectually, I knew that my parents were getting closer to the end of their lives, but emotionally, I was not ready.

Accept the help of those who have gifts and graces ...

When my niece, Kennetra, who has a degree in biology and chemistry, saw the chaotic assemblage of pill bottles, she went into action. She cleaned out a nice desk that looked like regular furniture and moved it into the kitchen. We went on a shopping expedition and bought a large dry erase board and colored markers. She organized a complete station for my parents' medications and hung the board above it on the wall with their entire medication regimen written on it. She also included a place on the colorful chart to initial who administered the last dose and at what time. This became totally priceless. We were able to administer our parents' evening medications without any difficulty.

The right kind of help ...

The nursing staff arrived bright and early Sunday morning. They clearly demonstrated the difference between skilled nursing care and our "amateur hour" efforts of care on that

125

previous Saturday. I was totally astonished at how effortlessly the staff transported our parents from their beds to their wheelchairs and served them breakfast. The night before, my sister and I had struggled to keep from dropping our mother. Unlike my sister, the "real nurses" did not need to hi-jack my mother's protective undergarment for extra leverage. Once my sister and I had huffed and puffed our mother into her bed, we all laughed and agreed that I would call the nursing service and ask them to start first thing in the morning. Thankfully, our brothers did not have any problems preparing our father for bed.

The day flowed so much better with the necessary trained help. We proceeded with the planned cookout, and several family members and friends visited with my parents all afternoon. However, my mother and father did not appear to recognize most of the family, even the ones they were once very close to. I realized after an hour or so that my parents were overwhelmed by the number of visitors and the level of activity. At some point, my father moved his wheelchair beside my mother's and held her hand. The nurse moved them into their bedroom where it was quiet and allowed only a few people at a time to visit. This worked better, and they seemed to enjoy the remainder of the evening.

My siblings and I had been wearing rose-colored glasses, but now we were face to face with the deterioration of our parents' ability to function. This was the last large family gathering with our parents before they passed.

Chapter 12

The Final Days

THE ROLLER COASTER ride appeared to be coasting along on somewhat level ground. My parents appeared stable after they adjusted to being home. We established a routine schedule with the nurse arriving early in the morning and staying until the late evening. Then, one of my siblings would stay overnight. I came in from Atlanta and stayed overnight, as well. This system worked out, for the most part.

Sometimes, my parents had quiet nights, while other nights were restless. One night, I was in a deep sleep, and I was suddenly awakened to the sound of a bed rail rattling and my father singing—quite loud. He repeatedly sang the words: "I am doing the best I can. I am doing the best I can." to an army marching rhythm. I sat up and listened before I tip-toed quietly to their room to check on them.

True enough, my father was singing and shaking the rails of his bed. This went on for half an hour until he finally went back to sleep. This was out of character for my father who was usually not a singer.

My parents engaged in limited activities, but spent most of their days napping between meals. It became harder and harder to watch them sleep their time away. I knew that their health was deteriorating despite the excellent care from the in-home staff and the visiting health care staff.

My last heart-to-heart conversation with my mother occurred about a week before her death. I was sitting beside her bed when I decided to tell her that she had a six-month-old great-grandson thanks to my 19-year-old son. I had made a conscious decision *not* to share that one of her beloved talented grandsons had gotten a young lady pregnant and dropped out of an expensive private university to produce and perform "trap music." I hesitated telling her because I was afraid that the stress of it all would kill her. It definitely almost killed me!

My mother had been dozing off and on, when I finally worked up the courage to tell her. She was awake with her head propped up on a pillow when I said, "Momma, I wanted to tell you that Allen has a baby."

She held her head up even more and looked directly at me with a puzzled look and asked, "How old is Allen?"

I responded, "Nineteen years old."

She put her head back down on the pillow and closed her eyes. There was a long pause before she opened her eyes and held her head up. She looked at me and asked, "What in the world does Allen need with a baby?"

I responded with one of her own all-time favorite answers when something made no sense. I said, "He needs a baby like he needs a hole in his head!"

She looked at me with a big, bright smile and started laughing. We both just laughed and laughed.

I had debated with my husband for the longest time about whether I should tell my mother or not. To be honest, maybe the real struggle was not about how she would respond, but more about my difficulty in accepting the situation. Six months earlier, I was so filled with hurt and embarrassment that I could not even talk about becoming a grandmother. I became even more of an emotional wreck after I found out that my son was dropping out of school to pursue his music dream. My stress level reached one of its highest peaks on the roller coaster ride during this time of additional family challenges. I struggled daily with the urge to bail out of my seat. I give all credit to God through prayer and meditation, along with my friends, C & C and LPC, for giving me the strength to stay buckled in.

Less than a week after my conversation with my mother, my youngest brother reported that the strangest thing happened on one of his overnight stays with our parents. He told me that before dawn, he heard a voice coming from our parents' bedroom. When he entered the room, he said that he almost passed out from the shock of what he saw. Our father was sitting at the foot of our mother's bed as if he was having a conversation with her. My brother stated that he knew that no one would ever believe him or could imagine what he had witnessed because it was not humanly possible given our father's physical circumstances. So, he quickly grabbed his phone and took a picture to show me and our siblings. Furthermore, he knew he would never be able to explain the complete scene. None of us could explain or understand how our father could have possibly gotten himself onto her bed. My brother explained that the rails on our father's bed were still up! Our father could not walk nor did he have the strength to pull himself out of bed. My brother told me that he asked our father, how he came to be sitting on our mother's bed. He said my father calmly stated that he walked. My brother said that he gently lifted my father in his arms and placed him back in his bed.

Emotionally shaken, my brother called to discuss his experience further with our other siblings and me after he sent the picture he had taken.

My husband and I both knew that this incident could not be explained in the natural. This was truly a miracle of God—that God had angels place my father on my mother's bed to say "Good-bye." Most of all, we knew in our hearts that we did not have long to say our own good-byes. We left as soon as possible to go see my parents.

When we arrived, my mother was conscious but very lethargic. I would like to think that she knew we were there, but I am not certain. As soon as we arrived, my husband conducted a medical examination. Although he had his toughest poker face on, I could see right through it and knew it was not good news. My sister and two of my brothers were there. He sadly told all of us that my mother was actively transitioning and estimated that she had about eight hours to live. He noted that it definitely would be less than twenty-four hours.

The hospice nurse came in right after my husband shared the information. She also examined my mother and agreed with my husband that it would be about eight hours or so, but definitely less than twenty-four hours.

We all seemed to weep quietly as we sat next to her bed. We had already called our brother in Alaska to let him know. My husband had to return to Atlanta to work at the hospital. He had been unable to find anyone to cover his patients. In addition, he was on call and was not supposed to be out of Georgia without full coverage. I did not have my car or any clothing. I knew that once my mother passed, I would not want to leave and then come back. I debated if I should leave or stay. I calculated in my somewhat confused state that if I left, I would have just enough time to get home, throw some clothes in the car and get back to Nashville before she passed. I convinced myself that I could achieve this unrealistic plan within eight hours or less.

When my husband and I left, I pressured him to drive like we were on the Atlanta Speedway rather than I-24. We made it to Atlanta in record time. I had made a list during the drive of what I needed to run into the house and grab before I hopped into my car and headed back to my parents. As soon as my husband turned into our driveway, my cell phone rang. It was my sister. She told me that our mother had just died.

I felt as if someone had knocked the wind out of me. I lost the ability to speak or catch my breath. My husband pulled into the garage, helped me out of the car and just held me tightly. Everything became a blur. I do not remember walking into the house or the passage of time.

I felt guilty for leaving my parents because I wanted to be there until the end. After talking with my sister, it became very clear that my mother did not want my siblings or me there when she left this world.

My sister shared that after I left, my brothers left with the intent of coming back in a few hours. She noted that after her daughter and grandchildren came over, she realized that she had not eaten or taken a shower. She stated that her daughter and the nurse encouraged her to go home. She left with plans to be back within the hour. My sister's grandchildren had not had anything to eat for a while and were hungry. So, my niece decided to take them to the McDonald's about ten minutes away and come right back.

Each time family members needed to leave, the nurse assured them that she was going to be right there in my parents' room. The nurse reported that my niece had been gone less than ten minutes when she walked out of the room to get something from the kitchen. She stated that she grabbed what she needed and walked back to the room to find that my mother had made her transition.

Interestingly, my father was asleep in his bed. And, so, only my mother and my father were in the bedroom when she took her last breath.

Knowing my mother, she transitioned the way she wanted with only my father present. My father slept quietly during and after her peaceful transition. There is no doubt that the night my brother found our father sitting on our mother's bed, he said his "Good-bye" and assured her that he would join her soon.

Photo Gallery

Young Love, Strong Love

Carolyn Chumley

James W. Lester, Sr.

Wedding Day
August 1949

Empty Nesters (Just The Two Of Us)

Growing Old Together

August 1999
Golden Wedding Anniversary
50 Years!

Four Generations of Strong Women
Carolyn Lester (seated in her church hat); LtoR:
Kennetra Price (granddaughter);
Kaelyn Price (great-granddaughter);
Linda Crutcher (daughter); Dr. Sherry Blake (daughter)

Dr. Sherry and Mother, Carolyn Lester

The Golden Years

My Father's Final Goodbye

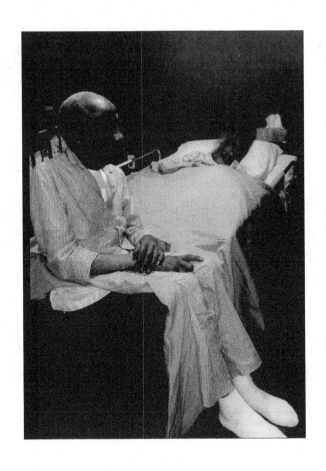

Chapter 13

Will This Ride Ever End?

YOU WOULD THINK that the roller coaster ride stopped at least for a moment after my mother's death. No, it did not. The ride slowed down to a creep, but it definitely did not stop. I wanted to jump off, but I leaned forward and pushed through my pain. So much happened at once–so many people called and stopped by to visit. All the activity became so much "white noise."

People were all around, but I felt as if I were totally alone. I heard story after story about how much my mother had helped people–from giving them food to clothing to money or whatever was needed. I realized just how much the community loved and appreciated my mother.

My father appeared to be in and out of awareness of my mother's passing. The nursing staff was instrumental in caring for him and sheltering him from the crowd of people and the stress of visitations and funeral arrangements. Although my siblings and I carried him early to view our mother's body, we all agreed that attending the funeral would be too much for him.

My mother's homegoing service was definitely a "Celebration of Life." It was a mixture of tears and laughter infused with her favorite gospel music. The church was packed with friends and family who came from near and far to honor and celebrate her. The outflow of love was both healing and overwhelming. While I was saddened, it became quite clear that both of my parents had helped countless people and given a life of service to the community. I was even more proud to be her daughter, and I realized that I was walking in her footsteps.

CAREGIVER'S TIP

Have a plan in place for your loved ones' funeral arrangements. Preplanned and prepaid funerals can help reduce your stress level at a highly vulnerable time.

After I had tied up as many loose ends as possible, I returned home to Atlanta–completely exhausted. My husband expressed concerns, but I reassured him that I was fine. After being back home for about a week, I was ready to return to work. My husband cautioned me to take some more time off saying that I wasn't quite myself. I hesitantly agreed to stay home a few more days, but I decided I was going to do some work from home. I called into the office and had someone on my staff drop off some paperwork. As I walked to answer the doorbell, I stopped in the kitchen to turn the water on in the island sink to thaw out the meat I had placed in there earlier. My intent was to turn it off after I answered the door. Instead, I walked to the mailbox and completely forgot about the running water. In fact, I walked through the kitchen on my way to our bedroom to start my paperwork and did not think to turn off the faucet.

A few hours had passed when my husband called and told me that he was pulling into the driveway, and he needed me to open the garage door. As I walked through the kitchen and made my way to the garage to press the garage button, all I could see out of the corner of my eye was water!

My husband heard me screaming as I ran back to the kitchen. Water was everywhere! It had flooded the entire kitchen area, all of the hardwood floors, as well as the carpeted areas in the living room. The water was standing over my ankles! As my husband ran to cut the water off, I ran and grabbed a bath towel. Yes, a bath towel.

CAREGIVER'S TIP

When you are overwhelmed with stress, things you do may not make sense or even be rational. Be kind and patient with yourself.

Not only did I grab a towel to soak up the water, I started lifting up the water-soaked bags of sugar and flour from the lower kitchen cabinets. Of course, sugar and flour were spilling everywhere! It was at this point that my husband told me to go and lie down and rest.

"Rest? I can't rest!" I thought wildly.

Instead, I asked my husband if I should call the insurance company. I am sure he said "Yes" just to get me out of the way. Then, he went downstairs to get the "wet vac."

When he didn't come back upstairs right away, I ran downstairs to see what happened. As soon as I stepped on the first step, all I could hear was the sound of water running. With each step, the sound of water was louder. I was crying hysterically by the time I was at the bottom step. The water had come through the ceiling and had pulled the paint off the walls in areas. Everything was ruined!

My dear husband was emptying the "wet vac" as quickly as he could. When he looked up and noticed me crying hysterically, he came over and wrapped his arms around me and said, "All this water is just your tears crying for your momma."

I melted into his arms and cried and sobbed uncontrollably. My husband reassured me that the things damaged were only material things and could and would be replaced. That was the beginning of my hard, grieving process for my mother.

I thought about my mother daily and cried often. I fell into a real funk, but I held it together on the surface. I had to remind myself that I was still blessed to have my father alive. Understandably, it was extremely difficult visiting my father without my mother being there.

Three months later, the repairs in our house were not completely finished. However, I had to attend a conference in Cleveland, OH. I was actually looking forward to sleeping in a room without the sounds and smells of construction work. In all my years of flying with Delta airlines, my luggage had never been lost until this trip. I arrived in Cleveland, but my luggage did not. And I had a little over three hours before I was scheduled to participate in an event at the conference. I must say that Delta understood the urgency of my situation, and the staff members were excellent in trying to help and accommodate me with a replacement budget. I was able to acquire the clothing I needed and get to my event on time.

While at the event, I was interrupted by a call from my sister. She told me that I needed to call our father's nurse and give permission to increase his pain medication and services. When I asked how he was doing, she was somewhat vague and ended the conversation quickly reminding me to call the nurse now. Because it involved medication for pain, I called the nurse immediately to avoid him being in any unnecessary discomfort. After the call, I reentered the event–with a funny feeling.

The next morning, I got up bright and early to start my meetings. Thank goodness my luggage had been located and delivered to my hotel room. I had just finished dressing when my phone rang. It was my husband telling me that my father's health had taken a turn for the worst and that I needed to go home to Nashville. He told me the arrangements had been made and my brand manager was going to call me with the details. My brand manager called as soon as I hung up from my husband and reassured me that

everything had been taken care of–from my flight to noti-
fying the conference leaders.

During my flight to Nashville, I convinced myself that
my father had died, and no one wanted to tell me. When I
arrived home, I was relieved to see that he was alive–though
barely. My father was semi-conscious and deathly ill. I was
shocked by the rapid decline in his health. After talking with
the nurses and my husband, I realized it was a matter of
time before he would pass. I stayed in his bedroom all night
and watched him slowly slip away. Early the next morning,
I had just walked out of his room when the nurse and my
sister called me back. As I entered his bedroom, my father
was taking his last breath. It was almost three months to
the day that my mother had died.

I found myself, once again, taking the long, slow, sad walk
in the funeral procession. This was all too familiar–the large
crowd, the tears, the tissues, the hugs and the overwhelming
support from family and friends. When my family and I left
the cemetery, I was a bag of mixed feelings. Relief was the
one sensation that I was embarrassed to admit feeling. Yes,
I was sad and distressed that I had lost both of my parents
within three months of each other, but I was emotionally
and physically drained.

*For the first time in more than ten years, the roller
coaster had finally stopped, and I was going to get off. I
had waited and longed for the day I could unbuckle my
seat. I was grateful that I was able to care for my parents
and will miss them forever. However, as I attempted
to unbuckle the clasp, the lash would not release.
Tears rolled down my face as I frantically attempted*

to unbuckle. I was burned out and confused. Then, I realized that while the roller coaster had stopped, I could not get off!

The death of my parents did not mean that the roller coaster ride was over. I was still buckled up, and the roller coaster was revving up to take off again—but to where? Little did I know that I was entering the tunnel of "Family Affairs." This is where you get a view of family members through a different lens, especially when money and dividing assets are involved. For me, the "Family Affairs" tunnel was full of surprises, disappointment, hurt and pain. I was definitely unprepared for any of this, especially given my parents had a will that seemed clear and straightforward. So, what could be the problem? Problem is an understatement.

Three years and counting after my parents' death, I am still in the tunnel. I can finally see a glimmer of light, but I have to complete the ride. I hope to help guide others through this tunnel to prevent and/or prepare them for the emotional distress. However, that will have to be a separate book–once I am totally unbuckled and off the roller coaster and have fully recovered from the 3Rs.

Emotional Survival Tip for The Release Phase

There's an old adage that says: "Once an adult, twice a child." A person is born as a child, grows to adulthood and reverts to a child or childlike state in old age.

Caregiving, for me, was the process of watching my parents revert to a childlike state and be in need of all the care and love as any child. They exited this world like they entered–helpless and vulnerable. My role as caregiver was to protect and nourish them through this journey.

Emotionally, the Release Phase is a strong reminder that ***we are born; we live; and we die***. Therefore, embrace every moment. And remember, this journey with your loved ones may be long or short. As they make their transition from this life, let go and allow them to start their new journey with dignity and grace.

CAREGIVING

Summary of Tips and Red Flags

The Caregiver's Tip Sheet

Helpful tips to get you through the ride

Phase I
Recognition: Pre-Caregiving

- If you are the primary caregiver/decision maker of a loved one, make sure you have the Power of Attorney (POA).
- Accept the role of the "Bad Guy."
- It is OK to say "No" to others' expectations.
- Do not be surprised by the various feelings you may experience, including anger, depression, anxiety, guilt, irritability and isolation.

Phase II
Reality: Caregiving

- Realize that you are human and can only do so much.

- Take care of yourself–do not ignore your personal health or needs.
- Ask for help when you need it.
- Find time on a regular basis to pray, journal, meditate or just be still.

Phase III
Release: Post-Caregiving

- Realize when you have done all that you can do and when it is time to let go.
- Allow yourself time and permission to feel.
- Realize the roller coaster ride doesn't end with the death of a loved one.
- Take care of yourself by detaching from any externally-generated emotional drama. In other words, do not get drawn into family controversies that have a detrimental effect on your ability to adequately carry out the wishes/desires of your loved one.

Some red flags that your loved ones may need help

It's not always easy to tell when your loved ones need more help. The following warning signs may appear before you notice a major decline in their ability to perform ADLs or IADLs:

- The house and yard aren't as well kept as usual.
- Things are out of place or in disarray.
- The refrigerator is empty or filled with old/ expired food.
- They are having problems with mobility or balance– leading to falls or bruises.
- They are forgetting or losing things frequently.
- They are easily confused.
- Their personal hygiene has declined.
- They are repeating questions or conversations within a short time frame.
- They are missing money or cannot account for all of their personal funds.

References

Greg Link, M.A. and Kenneth Hepburn, Ph.D. (2019, June 3). A-Z Health Topics, U.S. Department of Health and Human Services Office on Women's Health. Retrieved from https://www.womenshealth.gov/a-z-topics/caregiver-stress

Senior Planning Services (2016). Retrieved from https://www.seniorplanningservices.com/category/caregiving/

Made in the USA
Monee, IL
16 December 2021

85823107R00095